Specialist publishers of price guid

1959

C000133659

Collecto

Decimal Issues of the United Kingdom

(formerly <u>Check Your Change</u>)

By Chris Henry Perkins.

1st Edition © 2014

ISBN (printed version): 978-0-948964-11-4
ISBN (eBook version): 978-0-901170-22-4

A comprehensive UK decimal coin catalogue. Also including the current circulating English banknotes.

Special thanks to Lance Corporal M McKerlie, esq.

Errors and Omissions:

Every effort has been made to ensure that the information and price data contained within this book are accurate and complete. However, errors do sometimes have a habit of creeping in unnoticed, and with this in mind the following email address has been established for notifications of omissions and errors: info@rotographic.com. Readers within the UK can also call the telephone number below.

Rotographic International

www.rotographic.com
020 308 69996

In Association with
predecimal.com

TABLE OF CONTENTS

INTRODUCTION

BACKGROUND OF DECIMALISATION

LISTINGS

INTRODUCTION

Rumours frequently do the rounds about this coin or that banknote being worth huge amounts of money - a couple of years ago it was the dateless 20p and in February 2014 was the 2009 Kew Gardens 50p. Mostly, these rumours are unfounded and all they do is annoy coin dealers who end up taking call upon call from soon-to-be disappointed people! This book contains the facts and no Chinese whispers.

Decimal coinage first appeared forty-six years ago (the florin and shilling being replaced by the Ten Pence and Five Pence respectively, in 1968) but is often over-looked as it has yet to stand the test of time in the same way that the pounds, shillings and pence did. As time progresses, I believe that interest in decimal coin-age will increase and with this new interest will come a need for reference material. This book is designed to begin the process of compiling in-depth records of the modern money minted by the Royal Mint and printed by the Bank of England. Hopefully it will become a fundamental reference guide.

This book used to be 'Check Your Change' but as decimals have been with us for two generations and most of the types are not seen in general circulation, this title has now morphed into a comprehensive guide to UK decimal coins. Together with it's sister "Collectors' Coins" publication, both books cover UK coinage from George III to date.

This inexpensive book, with listings and colour pictures of every decimal coin type and circulating English banknote, should provide an excellent guide to modern coinage and as such, should aid existing collectors and hopefully stimulate new ones.

NEW IN 2014

Soon after the last (2011) edition of this book (in its Check Your Change guise) went to print, the Royal Mint issued a few (and I use the term 'few' very loosely) 50 Pence coins to mark the 2012 London Olympics. In total 29 different 50 pences were issued, featuring stylised and in the main, very cheap looking motifs representing the many different sports that make up an Olympic games. In my opinion this was too many coins in one go. Long forgotten are the days where special coins were only issued for coronations and jubilees - nowadays, anything that can generate sales has become significant. I do know however, that many people took on the challenge to try and source one of each from change, which was achievable, but only if you were quick and had also employed enough friends and family with the task of searching!

The Royal Mint also sold the 'London 2012 Sports Collection' 50 Pence coins in sealed plastic/card packages for around £3 each. Interestingly, they seemed to have rushed these out without final checks and on some of the Aquatics themed coins (which was coin no.1 out of the 29) a swimmer can be seen with distinctive water lines on her face. This seems to not have been what was intended and it was quickly rectified so that all of the circulation coins and most of the coins in packages were of a different design, without the lines on the face and with other minor changes. It is unclear how many of the 'error' coins with the lines on the face were released. I know of at least 20 to 40, but that low number may just be because the error isn't particularly clear - unless you happen to have two different coins side by side - and also the fact that the error coin only seems to have been put into the special packaging, so it's unlikely to have got into change and therefore the wider public wouldn't have seen it. No doubt after reading this, more will come to light (I'd be grateful for owners of the wavy-lines-on-face coin to let me know - please also see the 50p section).

In order to maximise sales revenue the Royal Mint, increasingly so over the last few years, are constantly exploring new strategies to sell more coins to the public. Usually this is done with themed coins that mark events or anniversaries. Clearly it's still not enough. Someone has put some pressure on the marketing department to think of news ways to maximise profits and as a result of this sales drive they have now taken to introducing completely new denominations that are not really intended to circulate as money. In 2009 a gold Quarter Sovereign was introduced (is that technically a crown, as one quarter of a pound?) and in 2013 a fine silver 27mm £20 coin was introduced which also features the Pistrucci St. George design. The Quarter sovereign has a face value of 25p, so with a gold value much higher (but less than half the purchase price) this coin is clearly not intended for circulation and should be viewed as a bullion issue.

The £20 coin contains about £7-8 worth of silver and is available for £20 (plus postage) however, the face value of £20 isn't actually recognised by banks or shops and even the Royal Mint web site made no mention of any coin above £5 having legal tender status until it was changed on their website during January 2014 (see also p.99). As far as I can tell, the silver £20 and the gold Quarter Sovereign are medallic issues and nothing to do with coinage. A pity, as I believe the nation's mint should primarily make coins to spend, rather than to sell. They are after all a government run body with an incredibly long and proud history. They have the state monopoly on making coins of the realm, not a profit!

Possibly during the same 'how to maximise profits' meeting, the Royal Mint has decided to change something which I feel puts collectors at a disadvantage. Unhappy with the competition between the many authorised Royal Mint re-sellers, which resulted in less control and slightly fairer prices for the products, the Royal Mint now seems to restrict sales of it's products to just a couple of large scale re-sellers, plus it's own sales department, which has its own marketing list. Coin dealers and other companies that have sold Royal Mint products for decades are now, pretty much overnight, told that they will no longer be supplied with Royal Mint coins. Some of these sellers are specialised in selling new coins and the Royal Mint products were the mainstay of their businesses. This seems highly unfair and monopolistic to me, and it will surely lead to higher asking prices over time, and of course more profit, assuming the public continue to buy their products. The Royal Mint now have their very own eBay account, which was established in January 2012!

The Royal Mint somehow managed to make a loss in the year to March 31st 2013, despite the plethora of coins issued in 2012. To cut costs in the future, the manufacture of gold sovereigns will be moved to India, which is no doubt to take advantage of cheaper labour and perhaps an easier supply of gold.

The future isn't really looking that rosy for the Royal Mint, and I do wonder if the collecting public is suffering because of this recent struggle. Suffering through being bombarded with far too many coins than is probably necessary. Suffering from the introduction of spontaneously made up legal-tender denominations that aren't legal tender and last of all, suffering from prices that are fixed and completely controlled by a monopolistic mint, that seems eager to thrust itself back into profit at the cost of coin collectors. In my opinion, the Royal Mint is completely lacking direction, jumping on to every possible bandwagon. All this, despite the main loss being caused, as far as I can tell, from international competition in one of their core business areas - the striking of coins on behalf of about 60 countries that have no national mint.

I do wonder if the public have finally realised that buying new issues isn't generally a very good idea and that it is best to either buy them a few years later when they have finished the inevitable plummet to a more realistic market level, or indeed, to obtain as many coins as possible, at face value from change.

There has been speculation about the government selling off the Royal Mint. That would raise a nice chunk of money for the coffers, but I fail to see how it would be good for coins. As it currently stands, there is scarcely any difference between the Royal Mint and privately operated for-profit mints who make their coins in the name of obscure lands, featuring anything popular, from cuddly animals to pop stars. Just how far would a privately run and entirely for profit Royal Mint go? Would they attempt to sell us cheaply made, ghastly colour-printed coins issued in the name of scantly populated Islands featuring Nelson Mandela on one side and Elvis Presley on the other (or anyone else popular enough and dead enough to not kick up a fuss about the use of their likeness)? And don't get me started on gold plated coins (see p.97)!

The Royal Mint are there to supply the public with coins, as per demand. I have nothing against them producing special packaging and selling year sets and special versions of current coins etc through a healthy dealer retail network and their own sales dept. The way things have gone though, and the way it appears to be heading, it's not looking good. At the very least, I'm going to need an awful lot more pages!

What do collectors of decimal coins really want? Who is able to keep up with the current volume of issues? Let me know.

I remain passionate about coins, but primarily those that are made to be spent, and not the pretenders that are labelled as coins but are essentially medallic issues made entirely for profit.

Now that I've had a good moan about the subject matter of my own book, I suppose I better get on with it!

C H Perkins, February 2014.

NEW IN THE 2011 (From the previous edition of Check Your Change)

Collectors had known about the 2008 20p featuring the new design but omitting date, for quite sometime and they were appearing on online auction sites for around £20-£30. In 2009 a private company with a misleadingly official sounding name offered £50 for each of the dateless coins.

This made national news and huge hype ensued. Everyone literally was checking their change! Coins were appearing on online auction sites and were genuinely selling for hundreds of pounds. Unfortunately this hype also attracted people with unrealistic hopes and almost as soon as the news broke to the wider public there were ridiculous listings of the error coins for overly inflated prices that appeared to be being bid on. As far as I'm aware none of the sales of over about £450 were genuine. The coins 'selling' for hundreds of thousands of pounds and higher, were not really changing hands at all....either not being paid for, or being bid higher deliberately.

What I found most shocking though is the unscrupulous criminal lengths that people went to in order to con the public! People were simply offering normal 2008 new design 20p's and making them sound like the dateless one by saying that: 'there is no date on the reverse' (which is correct and normal) and simply having a picture of one side. Other sellers were offering 2 different coins: an old type and a new type, but cleverly worded to imply that a heads side is dateless and so is a tails side. Some were simply using stolen pictures without actually having one of the coins and one seller actually filed off the date from a normal coin and was selling it as the dateless type!

USING THIS CATALOGUE

The values listed in this catalogue are the result of many hours of compiling and comparing the prices offered by online dealers, online auctions, dealer sales lists, live-auction catalogues, and other sources. For some items, there is such a limited number of transactions on which to base the values that they may seem conservative.

Values are in the main, only given for coins in uncirculated condition. The reason for this is that with the high mintage figures of virtually all coins covered in this catalogue, any coin that is not in uncirculated grade usually has virtually no value above the face value. As a matter of fact, some recent issues are so readily available that even in uncirculated grade, they sometimes have no value over face value. (such coins are listed as FV - Face Value). Please remember: **Most modern coins are only desirable in UNC condition, which means 'as new'.**

Note that for the lower valued coins, the time and effort needed to document, catalogue, and list these items for sale by a dealer is often not cost-effective, and thus it is often much more difficult to locate a particular coin than the low value would indicate. Prices for proof coins are for coin in their original Royal Mint packaging with associated paperwork.

MINTAGES

The numbers given as mintages are based on information available from many sources, including other reference works, online sources, and the Royal Mint. The accuracy of these numbers is by no means guaranteed, and modifications may be made as better information becomes available.

It should also be noted that for some of the later issues, the mintages given are the "maximum mintages", and the actual number of pieces struck may be currently unknown. Again, updates will be made when final information is available.

COIN GRADES

The listings in this catalogue contain three prices, where applicable. The guidelines for these grades are as follows:

Uncirculated (UNC) - Appears as it did when it left the Mint. There will be no signs of wear or handling. May show "bag marks", as is common for mass-produced coins.

Brilliant uncirculated (BU) - A high end uncirculated. Fewer "bag marks" visible. All of, or 95%+ of the mint lustre remaining. Most coins from Specimen folders or sealed packaging are considered BU.

Proof - A coin usually struck from specially prepared coin dies on a specially prepared metal blank. Proofs are usually given more than one blow from the dies and are usually struck with presses operating at slower speeds and higher striking pressures. Because of this extra care, Proofs usually exhibit much sharper detail than the regular coins, which are often called business strikes.

THE VALUE OF GOLD

At the time of writing this 2014 edition the price of gold on international markets remains historically high but has fallen quite significantly over the last year. The price of gold influences the gold coin prices quoted in this book. The prices quoted here are based on a gold value of about £760 per ounce (£24,500 per kilogramme).

THE DECIMALISATION OF UNITED KINGDOM COINAGE

Ever since the decimalisation of the French Franc in 1795, there was discussion and debate over the conversion of the British currency to a decimal standard. In 1849 the Victorians introduced the florin denomination which was worth two shillings, or one tenth of a pound, but it was not until the conversion of the South African currency in 1960 that any serious consideration was given to a complete changeover. Following the report of the Halsbury Committee (Committee of the Enquiry on Decimal Currency) in 1963, and approval of the recommendations of the Committee in 1966, a Decimal Currency Board (DCB) was created to initiate and carry out the plans, approved by Parliament as the Decimal Currency Act of July 1967.

The decision was made to keep the pound sterling as the core unit of currency, and to divide it into 100 equal units, retaining the "penny" name, but adding a "new" to help distinguish the decimal system from the £.s.d. system. By using this system, the shilling (which was worth 1/20th of a pound), became the equivalent of 5 new pence, and the florin (1/10th of a pound) became 10 new pence. This was a vital step in ensuring a smooth transition period, as the shilling and florin pieces remained in circulation for an extended period of time after "Decimalisation Day", which was the 15th of February 1971.

Three pre-decimal coins remained in circulation after "Decimalisation Day", including the florin and shilling mentioned above, along with the sixpence piece, which had a decimal value of $2\frac{1}{2}$ new pence (thus requiring the issuance of a $\frac{1}{2}$ new penny piece to accommodate its usage).

In 1972, the striking of a decimal base-metal commemorative crowns began, with a value of 25 new pence, which is the equivalent of 5 shillings (the pre-decimal value of a "crown"). Four issues were minted between 1972 and 1981. In 1990 the base metal crown returned, again, but with a re-valued face value of £5. They are all legal tender but seldom see circulation.

In 1982 a 20p coin was introduced. Interestingly, the Victorian Double Florin coin, which was struck from 1887 to 1890, was not officially demonetised in 1971 (as far as the author can establish) so thoretically you could spend a Double Florin as a 20p coin. To actually do so would be quite silly because the silver content of the said Victorian coin is probably worth at least £6!

In 1983 a £1 coin was introduced, and the £1 Bank of England banknote was retired as a cost-cutting measure (Scottish banks continue to issue £1 notes). With the increased popularity and usage of the £1 coin, in 1997 a circulating £2 bi-metal coin was first struck. £2 coins issued in the 1980s hadn't really taken off.

9

THE DECIMALISATION OF UNITED KINGDOM COINAGE

In 2008 new 'normal' (i.e. non commemorative, sometimes refered to as defini-
tives) British Coins appeared in circulation after the Royal Mint held a nationwide
competition to come up with the new designs. The new coins feature sections of
the Royal Shield, or the whole shield in the case of the £1 coin. Unusually, the old
established designs were also issued in 2008 resulting in two different 2008 coins
entering circulation for each denomination. The new design non commemorative
decimal coins are shown below.

From 2012 the 5p and 10p are made of nickel plated steel, which is cheaper than
the copper-nickel alloy which has been used for all silver coloured circulation coins
from 1947 onwards. The nickel plated 5p and 10p coins are now magnetic (post
1993 1p and 2p coins also have a steel core and are magnetic, with the exception
of some 1998 2p coins).

TIMELINE OF DECIMAL COINAGE

1968	Introduction of new portrait of QEII, by Arnold Machin. 5 new pence (shilling-sized) & 10 new pence (florin-sized) are introduced.
1969	The 50 new pence coin is introduced, to replace the 10 shilling notes. Pre-decimal halfpennies and half-crowns are demonetised.
1971	The 15th of February 1971 is "Decimalisation Day." $1/2$, 1 and 2 new pence are officially introduced (these were originally issued in 1968 & 1969 wallets). Pre-decimal pennies and threepence are demonetised. Proof sets of decimal coins are introduced.
1972	The first 25 pence commemorative crown is struck.
1973	The first 50 pence commemorative coin is struck.
1980	Pre-decimal sixpences are demonetised.
1982	The 20 pence piece is introduced. BU Annual Royal Mint folders are introduced. The word "New" is dropped from all coinage.
1983	£1 coins are introduced to replace the £1 note.
1984	$1/2$ pennies are demonetised.
1985	Introduction of new portrait of QEII, by Raphael Maklouf.
1986	The first commemorative £2 coin is struck.
1990	Pre-decimal post-1816 shillings and the large initial 5 pence are demonetised. At the same time a smaller 5 pence is introduced.
1990	The Crown is given a face value of £5 (instead of 25p) and the first commemorative £5 crown is struck.
1992	The 1p and 2p are changed from bronze to copper-plated steel.
1992	Pre-decimal florins and the large initial 10 pence are demonetised. At the same time a smaller 10 pence is introduced.
1997	New bi-metallic £2 coins are circulated.
1997	The new smaller 50 pence replaces the old large type.
1998	Introduction of the new portrait of Her Majesty the Queen, by Ian Rank-Broadley.
2008	Introduction of a complete range of new designs for use on all British decimal coins, 1p to £1.

What's currently legal tender?
No half pennies are legal tender any longer. They were demonetised on the 31st December 1984. Banks do accept them, but the high street financial institutions are not exactly falling over themselves to exchange the half-pee tiddlers!

Which are hard to find?
The 1972 coin was made as a proof only and went into sets, so is harder to find. The last coin, dated 1984, was also made for sets only.

OBVERSE

OBVERSE 1
(used 1971 - 1984)
D•G•REG•F•D•(date) || ELIZABETH II
Elizabeth II, Dei Gratia Regina, Fidei Defensor
(Elizabeth II, By the Grace of God Queen and Defender of the Faith)
Portrait by: Arnold Machin

REVERSE

REVERSE 1
(used 1971 - 1981)
Regal Crown
1/2 NEW PENNY
Design by: Christopher Ironside

REVERSE 2
(used 1982 - 1984)
Regal Crown
1/2 HALF PENNY
Design by: Christopher Ironside

INFO

Although it was known from the onset that the half-penny would see limited circulation, it was necessary to help facilitate the transition from 'old money' to decimal, as the old sixpence coins were still circulating as 2½ new pence.

TYPE 1 (obverse 1, reverse 1)

			UNC	BU	Proof
1971	1,394,188,250		£0.05	£0.20	£2.00
1972		Proof Only			£5.00
1973	365,680,000		£0.10	£0.50	£2.00
1974	365,448,000		£0.10	£0.50	£2.00
1975	197,600,000		£0.10	£0.50	£2.00
1976	412,172,000		£0.10	£0.50	£2.00
1977	86,368,000		£0.10	£0.50	£2.00
1978	59,532,000		£0.10	£0.50	£2.00
1979	219,132,000		£0.10	£0.50	£2.00
1980	202,788,000		£0.10	£0.50	£2.00
1981	46,748,000		£0.10	£0.50	£2.00

TYPE 2 (obverse 1, reverse 2)

			UNC	BU	Proof
1982	190,752,000		£0.05	£0.50	£2.00
1983	7,600,000		£0.50	£2.00	£2.00
1984	158,820	[2]	£2.00	£3.00	£3.00

DOCUMENTED ERRORS
1971 double-headed (mint error) £200

NOTES
[1]   Each year, it is determined, based upon supply and demand, what denominations will be struck for circulation. These years were not issued for circulation, and no "business strikes" were made.
[2]   These years were not issued for circulation, and the "business strikes" were made for BU mint folders, only.

What's currently legal tender?

All 1p coins are legal tender. Merchants are allowed by law to refuse payments made in 1p or 2p coins if the combined total value of the 'coppers' is more than 20p in any one transaction.

Which are hard to find?

The 1972 coin was made as a proof only and went into sets, so is not likely to be found in circulation. In 1992 the Royal Mint changed from using bronze to using copper-plated steel. In that year both types exist and the bronze 1992 is not usually found in circulation.

There is no 'NEW PENNY' error coin relating to one pennies. All 1971 to 1981 coins have 'NEW PENNY' on the reverse and all 1982 to date coins have 'ONE PENNY' on the reverse.... at least they should do! So far no errors have been reported.

OBVERSE

OBVERSE 1
(used 1971 - 1984)
D•G•REG•F•D•(date) || ELIZABETH II
Elizabeth II, Dei Gratia Regina, Fidei Defensor
(Elizabeth II, By the Grace of God Queen and Defender of the Faith)
Portrait by: Arnold Machin

OBVERSE 2
(used 1985 - 1997)
ELIZABETH II || D•G•REG•F•D•(date)
Elizabeth II, Dei Gratia Regina, Fidei Defensor
(Elizabeth II, By the Grace of God Queen and Defender of the Faith)
Portrait by: Raphael Maklouf

OBVERSE 3
(used 1998 - 2008)
ELIZABETH•II•D•G || REG•F•D•(date)
Elizabeth II, Dei Gratia Regina, Fidei Defensor
(Elizabeth II, By the Grace of God Queen and Defender of the Faith)
Portrait by: Ian Rank-Broadley

OBVERSE 4 (similar to last, with no rim beading)
(used 2008 to date)
ELIZABETH•II•D•G || REG•F•D•(date)
Elizabeth II, Dei Gratia Regina, Fidei Defensor
(Elizabeth II, By the Grace of God Queen and Defender of the Faith)
Portrait by: Ian Rank-Broadley

REVERSE

REVERSE 1
(used 1971 - 1981)
Crowned portcullis
[OFFICIALLY: A portcullis with chains
royally crowned]
1 NEW PENNY
Design by: Christopher Ironside

REVERSE 2
(used 1982 - 2008)
Crowned portcullis
[OFFICIALLY: A portcullis with chains
royally crowned]
1 ONE PENNY
Design by: Christopher Ironside

REVERSE 3
(used 2008 to date)
Lower left section of the Royal coat of
Arms of the United Kingdom.
ONE PENNY
Design by: Matthew Dent

TYPE 1 (obverse 1, reverse 1)

		UNC	BU	Proof
1971	1,521,666,250	£0.05	£0.20	£2.00
1972	Proof Only			£5.00
1973	280,196,000	£0.20	£1.00	£3.00
1974	330,892,000	£0.20	£1.00	£3.00
1975	221,604,000	£0.20	£1.00	£3.00
1976	300,160,000	£0.20	£1.00	£3.00
1977	285,430,000	£0.20	£1.00	£3.00
1978	292,770,000	£0.20	£1.00	£2.00
1979	459,000,000	£0.20	£1.00	£2.00
1980	416,304,000	£0.20	£1.00	£2.00
1981	301,800,000	£0.20	£1.00	£2.00

TYPE 2 (obverse 1, reverse 2)

1982	100,292,000	£0.20	£0.70	£2.00
1983	243,002,000	£0.20	£0.70	£2.00
1984	154,759,625	£0.20	£0.70	£2.00

TYPE 3 (obverse 2, reverse 2)

			UNC	BU	Proof
1985	200,605,245		£0.05	£0.70	£2.00
1986	369,989,130		£0.05	£0.70	£2.00
1987	499,946,000		£0.05	£0.70	£2.00
1988	793,492,000		£0.05	£0.70	£2.00
1989	658,142,000		£0.05	£0.70	£2.00
1990	529,047,500		£0.05	£0.70	£2.00
1991	206,457,600		£0.05	£0.70	£2.00
1992	78,421 ‡Al	Bronze	£3.00	£3.00	£3.00

TYPE 4 (obverse 2, reverse 2)
From now on, made of copper-plated steel (which is slightly magnetic)

		UNC	BU	Proof
1992	253,867,000	FV	£0.10	-
1993	602,590,000	FV	£0.10	£2.00
1994	843,834,000	FV	£0.10	£2.00
1995	303,314,000	FV	£0.10	£2.00
1996	723,840,060	FV	£0.10	£2.00
1997	396,874,000	FV	£0.10	£2.00

TYPE 5 (obverse 3, reverse 2)

		UNC	BU	Proof
1998	739,770,000	FV	£0.10	£2.00
1999	891,392,000	FV	£0.10	£2.00
2000	1,060,364,000	FV	£0.05	£2.00
2001	928,802,000	FV	£0.05	£2.00
2002	601,446,000	FV	£0.05	£2.00
2003	539,436,000	FV	£0.05	£2.00
2004	739,764,000	FV	£0.05	£2.00
2005	536,318,000	FV	£0.05	£2.00
2006	524,605,000	FV	£0.05	£2.00
2007	548,002,000	FV	£0.05	£2.00
2008	180,600,000	FV	FV	£2.00

TYPE 6 (obverse 4 reverse 3)

		UNC	BU	Proof
2008 ‡3	507,952,000	FV	FV	£2.00
2009	556,412,800	FV	FV	£2.00
2010	609,603,000	FV	FV	£2.00
2011	431,004,000	FV	FV	£2.00
2012	227,201,000	FV	FV	£2.00
2013		FV	FV	£2.00
2013 ‡4	In Silver	Royal Mint, price new		£28.00
2013		FV	FV	£2.00
2014 ‡4	In Silver	Royal Mint, price new		£28.00

NOTES

‡1 These years were not issued for circulation, and no "business strikes" were made.

‡2 These years were not issued for circulation, and the "business strikes" were made for BU mint folders, only.

‡A1 In 1992, a change in materials was made from bronze to copper-plated steel. In 1992 the original bronze planchets were only used for the BU Mint folders and Proof sets. The copper-plated steel planchets were used for circulation strikes only.

‡3 The Dent reverse 2008 1p has been reported to exist with incorrect die alignment.

‡4 Sterling Silver pennies struck by the RM and available in blue or pink pouches. for babies.

INFO

Arnold Machin (1911-1999), designed the bust portrait used on decimal coinage, starting in 1968, and used until 1984. It also appeared on the coins of many British Commonwealth nations, including Australia, Canada, and several others. He also designed the reverses of the 1972 Silver Wedding 25p and the 1977 Silver Jubilee 25p. Even with all of this global numismatic exposure, Mr. Machin is probably best known for his portrait used on British postage stamps since 1967, which is estimated to have been printed on over 150 billion stamps.

25.91 mm • 7.13 grammes • bronze • plain edge

What's currently legal tender?

All 2p coins are legal tender. Merchants are allowed by law to refuse payments made in 1p or 2p coins if the combined total value of the 'coppers' is more than 20p in any one transaction.

Which are hard to find?

The change from using bronze to using copper-plated steel has led to a couple of scarcer types. The 1992 coin made of bronze (i.e. not magnetic) is much scarcer than the 1992 coin made of copper-plated steel. The same kind of thing happened in 1998.

By far the rarest and most expensive 2p is the 1983 error coin, which has NEW PENCE on the back instead of TWO PENCE. This mistake just affects the 1983 2p; no other coins have been noted with this error. The error coins went into sets and were not generally circulated. It is possible though, that some of the sets were broken up before the error was noticed, so there may be a few £500 2p coins out there somewhere!

OBVERSE

OBVERSE 1
(used 1971 - 1984)
D•G•REG•F•D•(date) || ELIZABETH II
Elizabeth II, Dei Gratia Regina, Fidei Defensor
(Elizabeth II, By the Grace of God Queen and Defender of the Faith)
Portrait by: Arnold Machin

OBVERSE 2
(used 1985 - 1997)
ELIZABETH II || D•G•REG•F•D•(date)
Elizabeth II, Dei Gratia Regina, Fidei Defensor
(Elizabeth II, By the Grace of God Queen and Defender of the Faith)
Portrait by: Raphael Maklouf

OBVERSE 3
(used 1998 - 2008)
ELIZABETH•II•D•G || REG•F•D•(date)
Elizabeth II, Dei Gratia Regina, Fidei Defensor
(Elizabeth II, By the Grace of God Queen and Defender of the Faith)
Portrait by: Ian Rank-Broadley

OBVERSE 4 (similar to last, with no rim beading)
(used 2008 to date)
ELIZABETH•II•D•G || REG•F•D•(date)
Elizabeth II, Dei Gratia Regina, Fidei Defensor
(Elizabeth II, By the Grace of God Queen and Defender of the Faith)
Portrait by: Ian Rank-Broadley

REVERSES

REVERSE 1
(used 1971 - 1981)
Plumes in Coronet
[OFFICIALLY: The Badge of the Prince of
Wales, with his motto ICH DIEN]
2 NEW PENCE
Design by: Christopher Ironside

REVERSE 2
(used 1982 - 2008)
Plumes in Coronet
[OFFICIALLY: The Badge of the Prince of
Wales, with his motto ICH DIEN]
2 TWO PENCE
Design by: Christopher Ironside

REVERSE 3
(used 2008 to date)
Upper right section of the Royal coat
of Arms of the United Kingdom.
TWO PENCE
Design by: Matthew Dent

TYPE 1 (obverse 1, reverse 1)

		UNC	BU	Proof
1971	1,454,856,250	£0.05	£0.30	£2.00
1972 Proof Only ‡1				£4.00
1973 Proof Only ‡1				£4.00
1974 Proof Only ‡1				£4.00
1975	145,545,000	£0.10	£0.50	£2.00
1976	181,379,000	£0.10	£0.50	£2.00
1977	109,281,000	£0.10	£0.50	£2.00
1978	189,658,000	£0.10	£0.50	£2.00
1979	260,200,000	£0.10	£0.50	£2.00
1980	408,527,000	£0.10	£0.50	£2.00
1981	353,191,000	£0.10	£0.50	£2.00

TYPE 2 (obverse 1, reverse 2)

		UNC	BU	Proof
1982	205,000 †2	£2.00	£2.00	£2.00
1983	631,000 †2	£2.00	£2.00	£2.00
1983	Error, NEW PENCE reverse £600.00			
1984	158,820 †2	£2.00	£2.00	£2.00

TYPE 3 (obverse 2, reverse 2)

		UNC	BU	Proof
1985	107,113,000	£0.10	£0.50	£2.00
1986	168,967,500	£0.10	£0.50	£2.00
1987	218,100,750	£0.10	£0.50	£2.00
1988	419,889,000	£0.10	£0.50	£2.00
1989	359,226,000	£0.10	£0.50	£2.00
1990	204,499,700	£0.10	£0.50	£2.00
1991	86,625,000	£0.10	£0.50	£2.00
1992	78,421 †B1 Bronze	£3.00	£3.00	£3.00

NOTES

‡1   These years were not issued for circulation, and no "business strikes" were made.

‡2   These years were not issued for circulation, and the "business strikes" were made for BU mint folders, only.

†B1   In 1992, a change in alloy was made from bronze to copper-plated steel. The original bronze blanks were only used for the BU Mint folders and Proof sets. The copper-plated steel blanks were used for circulation strikes only.

†B2   In 1998, both bronze and copper-plated steel blanks were used. It is estimated that about 55% of the mintage was bronze.

†B3   In 1999, bronze blanks were used for Proof sets.

TYPE 4 (obverse 2, reverse 2) From now on, made of copper-plated steel (slightly magnetic)

			UNC	BU	Proof
1992	102,247,000		£0.05	£0.50	-
1993	235,674,000		£0.05	£0.50	£2.00
1994	531,628,000		£0.05	£0.50	£2.00
1995	124,482,000		£0.05	£0.50	£2.00
1996	296,276,000		£0.05	£0.50	£2.00
1997	496,116,000		£0.05	£0.50	£2.00

TYPE 5 (obverse 3, reverse 2)

			UNC	BU	Proof
1998	231,830,000	Copper/Steel	FV	£0.10	£2.00
1998	About 55% of total [B2]	Bronze	FV	£0.10	
1999	353,816,000	Copper/Steel	FV	£0.10	£2.00
1999	[B3]	Bronze Proof			£3.00
2000	583,643,000		FV	£0.10	£2.00
2001	551,886,000		FV	£0.10	£2.00
2002	168,556,000		FV	£0.05	£2.00
2003	260,225,000		FV	£0.05	£2.00
2004	356,396,000		FV	£0.05	£2.00
2005	280,396,000		FV	FV	£2.00
2006	170,637,000		FV	FV	£2.00
2007	254,500,000		FV	FV	£2.00
2008	10,600,000				

TYPE 6 (obverse 4, reverse 3)

		UNC	BU	Proof
2008	241,679,000	FV	FV	£2.00
2009	150,500,500	FV	FV	£2.00
2010	99,600,000	FV	FV	£2.00
2011	114,300,000	FV	FV	£2.00
2012	67,800,000	FV	FV	£2.00
2013		FV	FV	£2.00
2014		FV	FV	£2.00

INFO

The current minting facility at Llantrisant, Mid Glamorgan, was built in 1967 in order to meet the demand for the millions of coins needed for the conversion to the modern decimal system used in the United Kingdom.

What's currently legal tender?
Only the smaller post-1990 5p coins are legal tender. The older large coins can be paid into most UK bank accounts. The predecessor of the five pence, the shilling, should also be accepted at most UK banks as five pence. Check any shillings have no collectable worth using the Rotographic sister Publication "Collectors' Coins (predecimal issues)" before redeeming them at five pence face value.

Which are hard to find?
The old large 5p coins are no longer found in change (unless someone has managed to pass one off as a 10p, which sometimes happens). The scarcest are those that were made just to go into sets, or as proofs: notably 1972 to 1974, 1976, a few of the early and mid 1980s coins, and the last large 5p struck in 1990.

OBVERSE

OBVERSE 1
(used 1971 - 1984)
D•G•REG•F•D•(date) || ELIZABETH II
Elizabeth II, Dei Gratia Regina, Fidei Defensor
(Elizabeth II, By the Grace of God Queen and Defender of the Faith)
Portrait by: Arnold Machin

OBVERSE 2
(used 1985 - 1990)
ELIZABETH II || D•G•REG•F•D•(date)
Elizabeth II, Dei Gratia Regina, Fidei Defensor
(Elizabeth II, By the Grace of God Queen and Defender of the Faith)
Portrait by: Raphael Maklouf

REVERSE

REVERSE 1
(used 1971 - 1981)
Crowned Thistle
[OFFICIALLY: The Badge of Scotland, a thistle royally crowned]
5 NEW PENCE
Design by: Christopher Ironside

REVERSE 2
(used 1982 - 1990)
Crowned Thistle
[OFFICIALLY: The Badge of Scotland, a thistle royally crowned]
5 FIVE PENCE
Design by: Christopher Ironside

TYPE 1 (obverse 1, reverse 1)

		UNC	BU	Proof
1968	98,868,250	£0.08	£0.40	
1969	120,270,000	£0.10	£1.00	
1970	225,948,525	£0.10	£1.00	
1971	81,783,475	£0.10	£1.00	£2.00
1972	+1			£5.00
1973	+1			£5.00
1974	+1			£5.00
1975	141,539,000	£0.20	£1.00	£2.00
1976	+1			£4.00
1977	24,308,000	£0.20	£1.00	£2.00
1978	61,094,000	£0.20	£1.00	£2.00
1979	155,456,000	£0.20	£1.00	£2.00
1980	220,566,000	£0.20	£1.00	£2.00
1981	+1			£4.00

TYPE 2 (obverse 1, reverse 2)

		UNC	BU	Proof
1982	205,000 +2	£3.00	£4.00	£4.00
1983	631,000 +2	£3.00	£4.00	£4.00
1984	158,820 +2	£3.00	£4.00	£4.00

TYPE 3 (obverse 2, reverse 2)

		UNC	BU	Proof
1985	178,000 +2	£3.00	£4.00	£3.00
1986	167,000 +2	£3.00	£4.00	£3.00
1987	48,220,000	£0.10	£0.30	£2.00
1988	120,744,610	£0.10	£0.30	£2.00
1989	101,406,000	£0.10	£0.25	£2.00
1990	102,606 +2 See also footnote on p23	£2.00	£4.00	£4.00

NOTES

+1   These years were not issued for circulation, and no "business strikes" were made.
+2   These years were not issued for circulation, and the "business strikes" were made for BU mint folders, only.

| 18.0 mm • 3.25 grammes • cupro-nickel • milled edge |

OBVERSE

OBVERSE 3
(used 1990 - 1997)
ELIZABETH II || D•G•REG•F•D•(date)
Elizabeth II, Dei Gratia Regina, Fidei Defensor
(Elizabeth II, By the Grace of God Queen and Defender of the Faith)
Portrait by: Raphael Maklouf

OBVERSE 4
(used 1998 - 2008)
ELIZABETH II•D•G || REG•F•D•(date)
Elizabeth II, Dei Gratia Regina, Fidei Defensor
(Elizabeth II, By the Grace of God Queen and Defender of the Faith)
Portrait by: Ian Rank-Broadley

OBVERSE 5 (similar to last, with no rim beading)
(used 2008 to date)
ELIZABETH II•D•G || REG•F•D•(date)
Elizabeth II, Dei Gratia Regina, Fidei Defensor
(Elizabeth II, By the Grace of God Queen and Defender of the Faith)
Portrait by: Ian Rank-Broadley

REVERSE

REVERSE 3
(used 1990 - 2008)
Crowned Thistle
[OFFICIALLY: The Badge of Scotland, a thistle royally crowned]
5 FIVE PENCE
Design by: Christopher Ironside

REVERSE 4
(used 2008 to date)
Middle part of the Royal coat of Arms of the United Kingdom.
FIVE PENCE
Design by: Matthew Dent

INFO

As of December 31st 1990, the large
five-pence coins were demonetised.

TYPE 4 (obverse 3, reverse 3)

			UNC	BU	Proof
1990	1,634,976,005 [3]		£0.05	£0.20	£2.00
1991	724,979,000		£0.05	£0.20	£2.00
1992	453,173,500		£0.05	£0.20	£2.00
1993	56,945 [2]		£2.00	£3.00	£3.00
1994	93,602,000		£0.05	£0.20	£2.00
1995	183,384,000		£0.05	£0.20	£2.00
1996	302,902,000		£0.05	£0.20	£2.00
1997	236,596,000		£0.05	£0.15	£2.00

TYPE 5 (obverse 4, reverse 3)

			UNC	BU	Proof
1998	217,376,000	100,000 proofs	FV	£0.10	£2.00
1999	195,490,000		FV	£0.10	£2.00
2000	388,506,000		FV	£0.10	£2.00
2001	320,330,000		FV	FV	£2.00
2002	219,258,000		FV	FV	£2.00
2003	333,230,000		FV	FV	£2.00
2004	271,810,000		FV	FV	£2.00
2005	236,212,000		FV	FV	£2.00
2006	317,697,000		FV	FV	£2.00
2007	246,720,000		FV	FV	£2.00
2008	92,880,000		FV	FV	£2.00

TYPE 6 (obverse 5, reverse 4)

			UNC	BU	Proof
2008 [4]	165,172,000		FV	FV	£2.00
2009	132,960,300		FV	FV	£2.00
2010	396,245,500		FV	FV	£2.00
2011	50,400,000		FV	FV	£2.00
2012	339,802,350	Nickel plated steel	FV	FV	£2.00
2013		Nickel plated steel	FV	FV	£2.00
2014		Nickel plated steel	FV	FV	£2.00

NOTES

[2]   1993 was not issued for circulation, and the "business strikes" were made for BU mint folders, only.

[3]   A 1990 Silver proof set with both large and small type coins was issued. Value approx £25

[4]   The Dent reverse 2008 5p has been reported to exist with incorrect die alignment of up to 180 degrees!

What's currently legal tender?

Only the smaller post-1992 10p coins are legal tender. The older large coins can be paid into most UK bank account.s The predecessor of the ten pence, the florin or two-shillings, should also be accepted at most UK banks. Check any florins have no collectable worth using the Rotographic sister publication "Collectors' Coins" before redeeming them at ten pence face value.

Which are hard to find?

The old large 10p coins are no longer found in change. The scarcest are those that were made just to go into sets, or as proofs: notably 1972, 1978 and all of the large type coins from 1982 onwards. There are lots of known varieties for the Ten Pence, both larger size and current size. See the end of this section.

OBVERSE

OBVERSE 1
(used 1971 - 1984)
D•G•REG•F•D•(date) || ELIZABETH II
Elizabeth II, Dei Gratia Regina, Fidei Defensor
(Elizabeth II, By the Grace of God Queen and Defender of the Faith)
Portrait by: Arnold Machin

OBVERSE 2
(used 1985 - 1992)
ELIZABETH II || D•G•REG•F•D•(date)
Elizabeth II, Dei Gratia Regina, Fidei Defensor
(Elizabeth II, By the Grace of God Queen and Defender of the Faith)
Portrait by: Raphael Maklouf

REVERSE

REVERSE 1
(used 1971 - 1981)
Lion Passant Guardant
[Part of the crest of England, a lion passant guardant royally crowned]
10 NEW PENCE
Design by: Christopher Ironside

REVERSE 2
(used 1982 - 1992)
Lion Passant Guardant
[Part of the crest of England, a lion passant guardant royally crowned]
10 TEN PENCE
Design by: Christopher Ironside

TYPE 1 (obverse 1, reverse 1)

			UNC	BU	Proof
1968	336,143,250		£0.15	£0.50	
1969	314,008,000		£0.15	£0.50	
1970	133,571,000		£0.15	£1.00	
1971	63,205,000		£0.15	£1.00	£2.00
1972	‡1	Proof Only			£5.00
1973	152,174,000		£0.15	£1.00	£2.00
1974	92,741,000		£0.15	£1.00	£2.00
1975	181,559,000		£0.15	£1.00	£2.00
1976	228,220,000		£0.15	£1.00	£2.00
1977	59,323,000		£0.15	£1.00	£2.00
1978	‡1	Proof Only			£5.00
1979	115,457,000		£0.15	£1.00	£2.00
1980	88,650,000		£0.20	£1.00	£2.00
1981	3,487,000		£1.00	£4.00	£5.00

TYPE 2 (obverse 1, reverse 2)

			UNC	BU	Proof
1982	205,000 ‡2		£3.00	£4.00	£4.00
1983	631,000 ‡2		£3.00	£4.00	£4.00
1984	158,820 ‡2		£3.00	£4.00	£4.00

TYPE 3 (obverse 2, reverse 2)

			UNC	BU	Proof
1985	178,000 ‡2		£3.00	£4.00	£4.00
1986	167,000 ‡2		£3.00	£4.00	£4.00
1987	172,425 ‡2		£3.00	£4.00	£4.00
1988	134,067 ‡2		£3.00	£4.00	£4.00
1989	77,569 ‡2		£3.00	£4.00	£4.00
1990	102,606 ‡2		£2.00	£4.00	£4.00
1991	74,975 ‡2		£2.00	£4.00	£4.00
1992	78,421 ‡2		£2.00	£4.00	£4.00

NOTES

‡1   These years were not issued for circulation, and no "business strikes" were made.

‡2   These years were not issued for circulation, and the "business strikes" were made for BU mint folders, only.

INFO

As of 30th June 1993, the large ten-pence coins were demonetised.

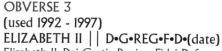
24.50 mm • 6.5 grammes • cupro-nickel • milled edge

OBVERSE

OBVERSE 3
(used 1992 - 1997)
ELIZABETH II || D•G•REG•F•D•(date)
Elizabeth II, Dei Gratia Regina, Fidei Defensor
(Elizabeth II, By the Grace of God Queen and Defender of the Faith)
Portrait by: Raphael Maklouf

OBVERSE 4
(used 1998 - 2008)
ELIZABETH II•D•G || REG•F•D•(date)
Elizabeth II, Dei Gratia Regina, Fidei Defensor
(Elizabeth II, By the Grace of God Queen and Defender of the Faith)
Portrait by: Ian Rank-Broadley

OBVERSE 5 (similar to last, with no rim beading)
(used 2008 to date)
ELIZABETH II•D•G || REG•F•D•(date)
Elizabeth II, Dei Gratia Regina, Fidei Defensor
(Elizabeth II, By the Grace of God Queen and Defender of the Faith)
Portrait by: Ian Rank-Broadley

REVERSE

REVERSE 3
(used 1992 - 2008)
Lion Passant Guardant
[Part of the crest of England, a lion passant guardant royally crowned]
10 TEN PENCE
Design by: Christopher Ironside

REVERSE 4
(used 2008 to date)
Upper left section of the Royal coat of Arms of the
United Kingdom.
10 TEN PENCE
Design by: Matthew Dent

TYPE 4 (obverse 3, reverse 3)

		UNC	BU	Proof
1992	1,413,455,170	£0.15	£0.20	£2.00
1993	‡CI	£0.15	£0.20	£2.00
1994	56,945 ‡2	£1.00	£4.00	£4.00
1995	43,259,000	£0.15	£0.20	£2.00
1996	118,738,000	£0.15	£0.20	£2.00
1997	99,196,000	£0.15	£0.20	£2.00

TYPE 5 (obverse 4, reverse 3)

1998	‡2 100,000 proofs	£2.00	£4.00	£4.00
1999	‡2	£2.00	£4.00	£4.00
2000	134,727,000	£0.15	£0.20	£2.00
2001	82,081,000	£0.15	£0.20	£2.00
2002	80,934,000	£0.15	£0.20	£2.00
2003	88,118,000	£0.15	£0.20	£2.00
2004	99,602,000	FV	FV	£2.00
2005	69,604,000 ‡CI 'I' of '10' to bead or space	FV	FV	£2.00
2006	118,803,000 ‡CI	FV	FV	£2.00
2007	72,720,000	FV	FV	£2.00
2008	9,720,000	FV	FV	£2.00

TYPE 6 (obverse 5, reverse 4)

2008	71,447,000		FV	FV	£2.00
2009	84,360,000		FV	FV	£2.00
2010	96,600,500		FV	FV	£2.00
2011	59,603,850		FV	FV	£2.00
2012	11,600,030	Nickel plated steel	FV	FV	£2.00
2013		Nickel plated steel	FV	FV	£2.00
2014		Nickel plated steel	FV	FV	£2.00

NOTES

‡2   These years were not issued for circulation, and the "business strikes" were made for BU mint folders, only.

‡CI   Varieties exist for the 1992 issue, see next pages Reverses 1 & 2 listed below have also been observed on 2005 and 2006 dated coins. It is not yet clear if one type is scarcer than the other.

TEN PENCE VARIETIES - Early, large size coins

There are a large number of subtle die varieties known for the Ten pences struck from the earliest in 1968, right through to the 1980s. The varieties first came to light in the 1970s, surveyed (among others) by Ron Stafford, who published a few incredibly detailed articles on them. The majority of the varieties concern the number of beads in the borders and the precise positioning of the letters and numbers, in relation to the border beads. It can make your eyes go funny just reading about it!

While significant, I feel that due to the complex nature, space required to list them all and the fact that the varieties are not often differentiated between, that it would perhaps be a better idea to list them on the Rotographic web site for advanced decimal coin collectors to see.

The 10p details will be listed on the 'Check Your Change' page: www.rotographic.com/check_your_change.htm

For those readers not online, please contact me using the contact details on the first page and I shall endeavour to send a paper copy to you. If enough readers request it, I'll include it as an appendix in a future edition.

TEN PENCE VARIETIES - Later, smaller coins

The production of the new 1992 smaller sized ten pence piece has yielded several varieties, some of which appear to be much less common than others.

The first type of ten pence pieces have a "wired" edge (left coin in both images), which has a curved edge, while all other varieties have a "flat" sharper edge (right coin in both images).

Obverse 1: The letters L and I in ELIZABETH point between 2 border beads. Obverse 2: The letters L and I in ELIZABETH point directly at border beads.

Reverse 1: The number 1 in the "10" points directly at a border bead. Reverse 2: The number 1 in the "10" points between 2 border beads.

TEN PENCE VARIETIES - Later, smaller coins

1992 Ten Pence types:

TYPE 1: wired edge, obverse 1 reverse 1
Earliest type. It appears that the "wired" edge was abandoned sometime around midway through 1992 production. Represents approximately 40% of total mintage.

TYPE 2: flat edge, obverse 1 reverse 1
A continuation of the TYPE 1, but on different planchets with flat edges. This type also represents approximately 40% of the total mintage.

TYPE 3: flat edge, obverse 1 reverse 2
An extremely uncommon variety, referred to as the "between/between" type. Represents about 3% of the total mintage, perhaps a little less. This type could become desirable in the future.

TYPE 4: flat edge, obverse 2 reverse 1
The rarest variety, referred to as the "to dot/to dot" variety. Represents less than 1% of the total mintage, with some estimates as low as one half of 1%. This type may be worth saving for the future.

TYPE 5: flat edge, obverse 2 reverse 2
This type exhibits a new obverse and reverse style. Represents approximately 15% of the total mintage. This is the type is found in Proof sets and BU Mint folders.

From 1993 to 2006 it seems that the circulation coins all have Reverse 1 (i.e the '1' of '10' pointing directly at a border bead) and that proof coins and coins in the BU sets have Reverse 2 (the '1' of '10' pointing between two border beads). It is not known 100% if this trend continued up to 2008 (the last year of the old reverse design).

21.40 mm • 5.00 grammes • cupro-nickel • plain edge

What's currently legal tender?

All 20p coins are legal tender. Victorian Double Florins also appear to be legal tender for 20p (4 shillings) as the author is unable to find any evidence that they were demonetised in 1971 with the rest of the old denominations. To spend one would be quite silly though, as the value of the silver contained within a double florin is far higher than 20p!

Which are hard to find?

The 1986 20p was made to be put in sets only and is therefore incredibly hard to find in change.

The new design 20p with no date is scarce. This coin is technically known as a mule and occured because the Royal Mint used the old obverse (OBVERSE 3) with the new reverse (REVERSE 2) in error, resulting in a coin with no date on it. All the errors should have been dated 2008 as the Royal Mint noticed the error after about 100,000 of the first coins were struck.

I get contacted a lot by people that have found one of these, hoping that they are worth £400+, as they were indeed selling for that much after the incredible amount of hype when the media first picked up the story and the public speculated. Collectors had known about them for months but the whole thing was blown massively out of proportion!

The approximate mintage number of the mule 20p claimed by the Royal Mint of 100,000+ would seem to be supported by the quite large volume of these offered for sale. Clearly this is a very low number of coins compared to all of the other 20p annual mintages! But 100,000 cannot really be deemed as rare. 1000 would be rare. 100 would be very rare. It should be borne in mind though, that rarity alone doesn't always lead to high values. High demand and not-enough-to-go-round is what causes things to be expensive. This is exactly what happened - all of a sudden thousands of people that wouldn't normally do anything with coins, apart from spend them, all wanted an error 20p!

Back to that low mintage number of about 100,000 - assuming that number is about right, it makes them approximately as scarce as the 1951 British penny. In the 1960s a similar thing happened (a little slower of course, because many people didn't even have televisions and the chap that invented the internet was still in short trousers) and the prices of known scarce coins were artificially inflated by people speculating that they would be a good idea to save for a rainy day. 50-odd years later an absolutely perfect shimmering BU 1951 penny is worth less than £100. I could be wrong, but I suspect the same will be true of the mule 20p in 60 years time. They will remain collectable, but the demand will never again outstrip the supply and as a result the values will stay at a more realistic level.

I also predict that in the future the near perfect examples removed from circulation early on will be more sought after than the majority of the coins that were taken from circulation at the point of maximum hype after being used and abused for 6+ months. The 20p is a popular coin and many that I saw for sale were far from perfect even after minimal circulation. Collectors are very fussy and always prefer the very best quality.

OBVERSE

OBVERSE 1
(used 1982 - 1984)
ELIZABETH II || D•G•REG•F•D
Elizabeth II, Dei Gratia Regina, Fidei Defensor
(Elizabeth II, By the Grace of God Queen and Defender of the Faith)
Portrait by: Arnold Machin

OBVERSE 2
(used 1985 - 1997, with a slight change in 1992)
ELIZABETH II || D•G•REG•F•D
Elizabeth II, Dei Gratia Regina, Fidei Defensor
(Elizabeth II, By the Grace of God Queen and Defender of the Faith)
Portrait by: Raphael Maklouf

OBVERSE 3
(used 1998 - 2008)
ELIZABETH II || D•G•REG•F•D
Elizabeth II, Dei Gratia Regina, Fidei Defensor
(Elizabeth II, By the Grace of God Queen and Defender of the Faith)
Portrait by: Ian Rank-Broadley

OBVERSE 4
(used 2008 to date)
ELIZABETH•II•D•G•REG•F•D•(date)
Elizabeth II, Dei Gratia Regina, Fidei Defensor
(Elizabeth II, By the Grace of God Queen and Defender of the Faith)
Portrait by: Ian Rank-Broadley

REVERSE

REVERSE 1
(used 1982 - 2008)
Crowned Tudor Rose
[The Badge of England, a royally crowned double rose]
20 TWENTY PENCE (date)
Design by: William Gardner

REVERSE 2
(used 2008 to date)
Lower right section of the Royal coat of Arms of the
United Kingdom.
TWENTY PENCE
Design by: Matthew Dent

33

TYPE 1 (obverse 1, reverse 1)

			UNC	BU	Proof
1982	740,815,000		£0.30	£0.40	£2.00
	Specimen in folder			£1.00	
1982	Silver Proof in case				£20.00
1983	158,463,000		£0.30	£0.40	£2.00
1984	65,350,965		£0.30	£0.40	£2.00

TYPE 2 (obverse 2, reverse 1)

			UNC	BU	Proof
1985	74,273,699		£0.30	£0.40	£2.00
1986	167,000 [2]		£4.00	£5.00	£5.00
1987	137,450,000		£0.30	£0.40	£2.00
1988	38,038,344		£0.30	£0.40	£2.00
1989	132,013,890		£0.30	£0.40	£2.00
1990	88,097,500		£0.30	£0.40	£2.00
1991	35,901,250		£0.30	£0.40	£2.00
1992	31,205,000 (both)	Small head*	£0.50	£1.00	£5.00
1992		Large head*	£0.30	£0.50	£2.00
1993	123,123,750		£0.30	£0.50	£3.00
1994	67,131,250		£0.30	£0.50	£3.00
1995	102,005,000		£0.30	£0.50	£3.00
1996	83,163,750		£0.30	£0.50	£3.00
1997	89,518,750		£0.30	£0.50	£3.00

TYPE 3 (obverse 3, reverse 1)

			UNC	BU	Proof
1998	76,965,000		FV	£0.50	£3.00
1999	73,478,750		FV	£0.50	£3.00
2000	136,418,750		FV	£0.50	£2.00
2001	148,122,500		FV	£0.50	£2.00
2002	93,360,000		FV	£0.50	£2.00
2003	153,383,750		FV	£0.50	£2.00
2004	120,212,500		FV	£0.50	£2.00
2005	154,488,750		FV	£0.50	£2.00
2006	114,800,000		FV	£0.50	£2.00
2007	117,075,000		FV	£0.50	£2.00
2008	11,900,000		FV	£0.50	£2.00

* The 1992 smaller head coin is slightly scarcer. The easiest way to tell the difference is that on the small-head coin the Queen's bust has a much sharper point where the neck ends at the bottom. The Obverse 2 picture on the previous page, is the smaller 'sharp neck' type.

MULE ERROR (mis-matching obverse 3 and reverse 2)

	UNC	BU	Proof
[2008] Also known as the 'dateless' 20p	£50	£75	-

Chinese made fakes exist. They have a dirty matt appearance, thinner lettering and a lack of detail.

TYPE 4 (obverse 4, reverse 2)

		UNC	BU	Proof
2008 [+3]	115,022,000	FV	£0.30	£2.00
2009	121,625,300	FV	£0.30	£2.00
2010	112,875,500	FV	£0.30	£2.00
2011	191,625,000	FV	FV	£2.00
2012	69,650,030	FV	FV	£2.00
2013		FV	FV	£2.00
2014		FV	FV	£2.00

NOTES

[+2]   Each year, it is determined, based upon supply and demand, what denominations will be struck for circulation. 1986 was not issued for circulation, and the "business strikes" were made for BU mint folders, only.

[+3]   The 2008 new design (non mule) coin and also some 2009 coins exist with what was originally thought to be a small raised 'I' on the reverse. It is probably actually a die crack, rather than any deliberate mint identification. Interesting nonetheless, as a few of these are known to exist. This same 'I' die crack coin has also been reported dated 2010, but is yet to be confirmed.

2008 20p reverse with small 'I'.

Historically the Crown is five shillings (one quarter of a 20 shilling pound). Therefore the new decimal crowns had a face value of 25p. These four commemorative crown coins are legal tender for 25p, but they are rarely used by the public, probably because they are too big to be convenient, and to collectors they are usually worth a little more than face value. Members of the public often assume incorrectly that these four coins have a face value of £5, due to the fact that the crown was re-valued to £5 in 1990 although the size of the coin remained the same.

For later Crowns, see the FIVE POUNDS section.

These four coins were issued to mark the following occasions: 1972 – The 25th Wedding Anniversary of the Queen and Prince Philip. 1977 - The Silver Jubilee of the Queen. 1980 - The 80th Birthday of the Queen Mother. 1981 - The Royal Wedding of Charles and Diana.

COMMEMORATIVE TYPE 1
Obverse: Standard portrait of QE II
Design by: Arnold Machin

Reverse: Elizabeth and Philip,
20 November 1947-1972
Design by: Arnold Machin

			UNC	BU	Proof
1972	7,452,100		£1.00	£1.50	£4.00
	100,000	.925 sterling silver proof			£20.00

COMMEMORATIVE TYPE 2
Obverse: Equestrian portrait of QE II
Design by: Arnold Machin

Reverse: Ampulla and anointing spoon,
items used during the Coronation
Design by: Arnold Machin

		UNC	BU	Proof
1977	37,061,160	£0.50	£1.00	£4.00
	Specimen in folder		£1.00	
	377,000	.925 sterling silver proof		£15.00

COMMEMORATIVE TYPE 3
Obverse: Standard portrait of QE II
Design by: Arnold Machin

Reverse: Portrait of Queen Mother,
surrounded by bows and lions
Design by: Richard Guyatt

1980	9,306,000	-	£1.00	£2.00	-
	Specimen in folder			£2.00	
	83,672	.925 sterling silver proof			£20.00

COMMEMORATIVE TYPE 4
Obverse: Standard portrait of QE II
Design by: Arnold Machin

Reverse: Conjoined busts of
Charles & Diana
Design by: Philip Nathan

1981	26,773,600	-	£1.00	£2.00	-
	Specimen in folder			£2.00	
	218,000	.925 sterling silver proof			£20.00
Set of 4 (72, 77, 80 and 81) Crowns as silver proofs in large case. 5000 sets issued					£65.00

37

What's currently legal tender?
Only the smaller (post-1997) 50p coins are legal tender now. Most banks will allow you to pay in the pre-1997 larger 30mm coins.

Which are hard to find?
The larger pre-1997 coins are not found in circulation. The most significant 50p that could possibly be found in change is the withdrawn Olympic Aquatics coin with the lines on the swimmers' face. See Commemorative Type 17.

OBVERSE

OBVERSE 1
(used 1969 - 1972, 1974 - 1984)
D•G•REG•F•D•(date) | | ELIZABETH II
Elizabeth II, Dei Gratia Regina, Fidei Defensor
(Elizabeth II, By the Grace of God Queen and Defender of the Faith)
Portrait by: Arnold Machin

OBVERSE 2
(used 1985 - 1997)
ELIZABETH II | | D•G•REG•F•D•(date)
Elizabeth II, Dei Gratia Regina, Fidei Defensor
(Elizabeth II, By the Grace of God Queen and Defender of the Faith)
Portrait by: Raphael Maklouf

REVERSE

REVERSE 1
(used 1969 - 1972, 1974 - 1981)
Britannia
[The seated figure of Britannia]
50 NEW PENCE
Design by: Christopher Ironside

REVERSE 2
(used 1982 - 93, 1995 - 1997)
Britannia
[The seated figure of Britannia]
50 FIFTY PENCE
Design by: Christopher Ironside

Britannia - TYPE 1 (obverse 1, reverse 1)

		UNC	BU	Proof
1969	188,400,000	£1.00	£2.00	
1970	19,461,500	£1.00	£4.00	
1971	‡1 Proof Only			£5.00
1972	‡1 Proof Only			£5.00
1974	‡1 Proof Only			£5.00
1975	‡1 Proof Only			£5.00
1976	43,746,500	£1.00	£3.00	£4.00
1977	49,536,000	£1.00	£3.00	£4.00
1978	72,005,500	£1.00	£3.00	£4.00
1979	58,680,000	£1.00	£3.00	£4.00
1980	89,086,000	£1.00	£3.00	£4.00
1981	74,002,000	£1.00	£3.00	£4.00

Britannia - TYPE 2 (obverse 1, reverse 2)

		UNC	BU	Proof
1982	51,312,000	£1.00	£3.00	£4.00
1983	62,824,904	£1.00	£3.00	£4.00
1984	158,820 ‡2	£2.00	£5.00	£5.00

Britannia - TYPE 3 (obverse 2, reverse 2)

		UNC	BU	Proof
1985	682,103	£2.00	£4.00	£5.00
1986	167,000 ‡2	£3.00	£5.00	£5.00
1987	172,425 ‡2	£3.00	£5.00	£5.00
1988	134,067 ‡2	£3.00	£5.00	£5.00
1989	77,569 ‡2	£3.00	£5.00	£5.00
1990	102,606 ‡2	£3.00	£5.00	£5.00
1991	74,975 ‡2	£3.00	£5.00	£5.00
1992	78,421 ‡2	£3.00	£5.00	£5.00
1993	56,945 ‡2	£3.00	£5.00	£5.00
1994	Marked 'ROYAL MINT TRIAL'	£600.00*		
1995	105,647 ‡2	£3.00	£5.00	£5.00
1996	86,501 ‡2	£3.00	£5.00	£5.00
1997	‡2	£3.00	£5.00	£5.00

NOTES

‡1   These years were not issued for circulation, and no "business strikes" were made.

‡2   These years were not issued for circulation, and the "business strikes" were made for BU mint folders, only.

*   Extremely rare 1994 'ROYAL MINT TRIAL' coins exist. The standard design is used. One known trial is round, not 7-sided. Not to be confused with commemorative type 3, which is also dated 1994!

27.3 mm • 8.0 grammes • cupro-nickel • plain edge

OBVERSE

OBVERSE 3
(used 1997)
ELIZABETH II || D•G•REG•F•D•(date)
Elizabeth II, Dei Gratia Regina, Fidei Defensor
(Elizabeth II, By the Grace of God Queen and Defender of the Faith)
Portrait by: Raphael Maklouf

OBVERSE 4
(used 1998 - 2008 and for some commemorative Fifty Pences)
ELIZABETH II || D•G•REG•F•D•(date)
Elizabeth II, Dei Gratia Regina, Fidei Defensor
(Elizabeth II, By the Grace of God Queen and Defender of the Faith)
Portrait by: Ian Rank-Broadley

OBVERSE 5 (similar to last, with different alignment)
(used 2008 to date with Reverse 4)
ELIZABETH II || D•G•REG•F•D•(date)
Elizabeth II, Dei Gratia Regina, Fidei Defensor
(Elizabeth II, By the Grace of God Queen and Defender of the Faith)
Portrait by: Ian Rank-Broadley

REVERSE

REVERSE 3
(used 1997 - 2008)
Often referred to as the 'Britannia issue' to distinguish it from the
commemorative issues.
[The seated figure of Britannia]
50 FIFTY PENCE
Design by: Christopher Ironside

REVERSE 4
(used 2008 to date)
Bottom section of the Royal coat of Arms of the
United Kingdom.
FIFTY PENCE
Design by: Matthew Dent

Britannia - TYPE 4 (obverse 3, reverse 3)

		UNC	BU	Proof
1997	456,364,100	£1.00	£2.00	

Britannia - TYPE 5 (obverse 4, reverse 3)

		UNC	BU	Proof
1998	64,306,500	£1.00	£2.00	
1999	24,905,000	£1.00	£2.00	£3.00
2000	27,915,500	£1.00	£2.00	£3.00
2001	84,998,500	£1.00	£2.00	£3.00
2002	23,907,500	£1.00	£2.00	£3.00
2003	23,583,000	£1.00	£2.00	£3.00
2004	35,315,500	£1.00	£2.00	£3.00
2005	30,354,500	£1.00	£2.00	£3.00
2006	24,567,000	£1.00	£2.00	£3.00
2007	11,200,000	£1.00	£2.00	£3.00
2008	3,500,000	£1.00	£2.00	£3.00

New non-commemerative - TYPE 6 (obverse 5, reverse 4)

		UNC	BU	Proof
2008	22,747,000	FV	£1.00	£3.00
2009		FV	£1.00	£3.00
2010		FV	£1.00	£3.00
2011		FV	£1.00	£3.00
2012	32,300,030	FV	FV	£3.00
2013		FV	FV	£3.00
2014		FV	FV	£3.00

DOCUMENTED ERRORS
1969 double-headed (minting error) £150+
19?? undated "double-tailed" (minting error) £200+

INFO

The "straight" edges of the 50p (and the 20p) are not flat, but arced to form a Reuleaux polygon. Any point on an arced edge is an equal distance from the opposing vertex. This design enables the coins to be used in vending machines.

41

30 mm • 13.5 grammes • cupro-nickel • plain edge

COMMEMORATIVE TYPE 1
1973 || 50 || pence (centre)
Nine clasped hands forming a circle
(Britain's entry into the European
Economic Community)
Reverse design by: David Wynne

		UNC	BU	Proof
1973	89,775,000	£1.00	£2.00	£4.00
	Proof in leatherette case			£4.00
	thick planchet but not recorded as Piedfort			-

COMMEMORATIVE TYPE 2
1992-1993 (upper) || 50 pence (lower)
Conference table with seats and stars
(completion of the EC single market and
the British Presidency)
Reverse design by: Mary Milner Dickens

		UNC	BU	Proof
1992-1993	109,000	£10.00	£12.00	£12.00
	Specimen in folder (including Britannia issue)		£14.00	
	26,890	.925 sterling silver proof		£24.00
	15,000	.925 sterling silver piedfort proof		£45.00
	1,864	.917 gold proof		£600.00

COMMEMORATIVE TYPE 3
50 pence (lower right)
Ships and planes taking part in the
D-Day landings
(50th Anniversary of the D-Day Invasion)
Reverse design by: John Mills

		UNC	BU	Proof
1994	6.705,520	£1.00	£2.00	£4.00
	Specimen in folder		£2.00	
	40,500	.925 sterling silver proof		£24.00
	10,000	.925 sterling silver piedfort proof		£30.00
	1,877	.917 gold proof		£600.00

COMMEMORATIVE TYPE 4
1973 EU 1998 | | 50 pence (lower)
Fireworks pattern of 12 stars
(25th Anniversary - UK entry into EEC)
Design by: John Mills

		UNC	BU	Proof
1998	5,043,000	£1.00	£2.00	£5.00
	Specimen in folder (including Britannia issue)		£7.00	
8,854	.925 sterling silver proof			£30.00
5,117	.925 sterling silver piedfort proof			£40.00
1,177	.917 gold proof			£450.00

COMMEMORATIVE TYPE 5
FIFTIETH ANNIVERSARY (upper) | | 50 pence (lower)
Caring Hands, holding sun's rays
(50th Annirversary - National Health Service)
Design by: Mary Milner Dickens

		UNC	BU	Proof
1998	5,001,000	£1.00	£2.00	£5.00
	Specimen in folder		£3.00	
9,029	.925 sterling silver proof			£20.00
5,117	.925 sterling silver piedfort proof			£30.00
651	.917 gold proof			£450.00

COMMEMORATIVE TYPE 6
1850-2000 (upper) || PUBLIC LIBRARIES (lower)
Open book upon pillared building
(150th Anniversary - British Libraries)
Design by: Mary Milner Dickens

			UNC	BU	Proof
2000	11,263,000		£1.00	£3.00	£5.00
		Specimen in folder		£4.00	
		.925 sterling silver proof			£20.00
	5,721	.925 sterling silver piedfort proof			£30.00
	710	.917 gold proof			£475.00

COMMEMORATIVE TYPE 7
50 pence (left) || 1903-2003 (lower right)
Suffragette with WSPU banner
(100th Anniversary - Women's Social and Political Union)
Design by: Mary Milner Dickens

			UNC	BU	Proof
2003	3,124,030	(43,513 proofs in sets)	£1.00	£3.00	£5.00
	9,582	Specimen in folder		£4.00	
	6,267 of 15k	.925 sterling silver proof			£20.00
	6,795 of 7.5k	.925 sterling silver piedfort proof			£30.00
	942 of 1000	.917 gold proof			£475.00

COMMEMORATIVE TYPE 8
50 pence (lower)
Runner's legs and stopwatch
(50th Anniversary - Roger Bannister's 4-minute mile run)
Design by: James Butler

			UNC	BU	Proof
2004	9,032,500	(35,020 proofs in sets) £0.80		£3.00	£5.00
	10,371	Specimen in folder		£4.00	
	4,924 of 15k	.925 sterling silver proof			£20.00
	4,054 of 7.5k	.925 sterling silver piedfort proof			£30.00
	644 of 1,250	.917 gold proof			£475.00

COMMEMORATIVE TYPE 9
50 (upper) || JOHNSON'S DICTIONARY 1755 (lower)
Dictionary entries for Fifty and Pence
(250th Anniversary - Samuel Johnson's English Dictionary)
Design by: Tom Phillips

			UNC	BU	Proof
2005	17,649,000	(40,563 proofs in sets) £1.00		£2.00	£5.00
		Specimen in folder		£3.00	
	4,029 of 7,500	.925 sterling silver proof			£20.00
	3,808 of 5,000	.925 sterling silver piedfort proof			£30.00
	1,000	.917 gold proof			£475.00

COMMEMORATIVE TYPE 10
FIFTY PENCE (lower)
Representation of the heroic acts performed by VC recipients
(150th Anniversary - Institution of the Victoria Cross)
Design by: Clive Duncan

			UNC	BU	Proof
2006	10,000,500	(37,689 proofs in sets) £1.00		£2.00	£5.00
	31,266	Specimen in folder		£5.00	
	6,872 of 7,500	.925 sterling silver proof			£20.00
	3,415 of 5,000	.925 sterling silver piedfort proof			£40.00
	804 of 1000	.917 gold proof			£475.00

COMMEMORATIVE TYPE 11
VC || FIFTY PENCE
The obverse and reverse of the Victoria Cross
(150th Anniversary - Institution of the Victoria Cross)
Design by: Claire Aldridge

			UNC	BU	Proof
2006	12,087,000	(37,689 proofs in sets) £1.00		£2.00	£5.00
	37,176	Specimen in folder		£3.00	
	6,310 of 7,500	.925 sterling silver proof			£20.00
	3,532 of 5,000	.925 sterling silver piedfort proof			£30.00
	866 of 1000	.917 gold proof			£475.00

27.3 mm • 8.0 grammes • cupro-nickel • plain edge

FIFTY PENCE | 1907 | BE PREPARED | 2007
The scouting badge
(100th Anniversary - The Scout Movement)
Design by: Kerry Jones

				UNC	BU	Proof
2007	7,710,750	(38,215 proofs in sets)	£1.00		£2.00	£5.00
	46,632 of 100k	Specimen in folder			£5.00	
	10,895 of 12,500	.925 sterling silver proof				£22.00
	1,555 of 5,000	.925 sterling silver piedfort proof				£40.00
	1,250	.917 gold proof				£475.00

1759 2009 | KEW
Chinese Pagoda
(250th Anniversary - Kew Gardens)
Design by: Christopher Le Brun

			UNC	BU	Proof
2009	210,000	(34,438 proofs in sets)	£30.00*	£50.00*	£120.00*
	128,364	Specimen in folder		£90.00*	
		.925 sterling silver proof			£150.00*
		.925 sterling silver piedfort proof			£200.00*
	1,000	.917 gold proof			£500.00

* Prices for these are currently inflated due to an article in the Daily Mail online on the 20th February 2014 following a Royal Mint press release. Similar information was repeated by the Guardian and also featured the following day on BBC Radio 2. The article implied that they are somehow special and this caused people to pay way over the odds on eBay, which in turn meant that sellers started pricing them higher and it all got a bit out of control. The normal non proof coins were selling for £180 at one stage (and nearly £300 for the specimen in folder). Just a couple of days later the normal non proof coins were down to between £35 and £50. It's a repeat of the ridiculous hype surrounding the dateless (2008) 20p mule error which caused that particular coin to sell for hundreds of pounds before dropping back to a more realistic £40 - £50 level (which, for most of the battered and abused coins that are sold is still too high in my opinion).

I predict it's future value may stay at a level a little higher than it was previously, perhaps £20 - £30 for a BU coin. The fact that people are aware of it, will probably have a residual effect on values.

A mintage of 210,000 (it's actually 444,696 if the packaged coins and those in the BU sets are included) is low compared the other Fifty-Pences that are currently in circulation, but there are plenty to go round, as there simply aren't anywhere near 444k people in the world that really want one, and one to keep, not to turn a profit on. Wait for prices to level off before buying!

COMMEMORATIVE TYPE 14 (previously no. 15 and incorrectly listed as dated 2010)
50 PENCE
An Olympic High Jumper - Obverse dated 2009
(The young viewers of Blue Peter were invited to submit entries for the design - This was the winner)
Design by: Florence Jackson (aged 8)
Obverse: 4

		UNC	BU
2009		FV	£1.00
	Specimen in folder		£8.00

COMMEMORATIVE TYPE 15 (previously 14)
CELEBRATING ONE HUNDRED YEARS OF GIRLGUIDING UK| 50 | PENCE
Girl Guide emblems
(100th Anniversary - The Girl Guides)
Design by: Jonathan Evans and Donna Hainan

		UNC	BU	Proof
2010	7,410,090	FV	£1.00	
	Specimen in folder		£7.00	
	.925 sterling silver proof			£30.00
	.925 sterling silver piedfort proof			£55.00
	.917 gold proof			£575.00

COMMEMORATIVE TYPE 16
WWF / 2011
Animal shapes
(50th Anniversary - Word Wildlife Fund)
Design by: Matthew Dent

		UNC	BU	Proof
2011	3,400,000	FV	£1.00	£5.00
	Specimen in folder		£5.00	
	.925 sterling silver proof			£20.00
	.925 sterling silver piedfort proof			£40.00
1,000	.917 gold proof			£600.00

47

27.3 mm • 8.0 grammes • cupro-nickel • plain edge

COMMEMORATIVE TYPE 17 (Olympic 1)
50 PENCE
Swimmer
[London 2012 Olympics - Aquatics]
Design by: Jonathan Olliffe
Obverse: 4

		UNC	BU
2011	1,010,000	FV	£1.00
	Specimen sealed on card		£2.00
	Withdrawn coin. Error - lines on face, right image		£900.00*

* The actual error coin in the picture above was sold by Rotographic on eBay, 27th Ferbruary 2014 to the top bidder for £908.88. Not very many are known so the values are likely to vary, as and when they come up for sale. As far as I know, this is one of the highest values on record for a decimal base metal coin.

COMMEMORATIVE TYPE 18 (Olympic 2)
50 PENCE
Hand Pulling an Arrow
[London 2012 Olympics - Archery]
Design by: Piotr Powaga
Obverse: 4

		UNC	BU
2011	1,010,000	FV	£0.75
	Specimen sealed on card		£1.00

COMMEMORATIVE TYPE 19 (Olympic 3)
50 PENCE
An Olympic High jumper - Obverse dated 2011
[London 2012 Olympics - Athletics, see also Commemorative type 14)
Design by: Florence Jackson (aged 8)
Obverse: 4

		UNC	BU
2011	1,010,000	FV	£1.00
	Specimen sealed on card		£1.50

COMMEMORATIVE TYPE 20 (Olympic 4)
50 PENCE
Shuttlecock
(London 2012 Olympics - Badminton)
Design by: Emma Kelly
Obverse: 4

		UNC	BU
2011	1,005,000	FV	£1.00
	Specimen sealed on card		£2.00

COMMEMORATIVE TYPE 21 (Olympic 5)
50 PENCE
Players on Ball-Textured Background
(London 2012 Olympics - Basketball)
Design by: Sarah Payne
Obverse: 4

		UNC	BU
2011	1,748,000	£1.00	£3.00
	Specimen sealed on card		£7.00
	.925 Silver Proof - See note, page 59		£20.00

COMMEMORATIVE TYPE 22 (Olympic 6)
50 PENCE
Player
(London 2012 Olympics - Boccia)
Design by: Justin Chung
Obverse: 4

		UNC	BU
2011	1,005,000	FV	£0.75
	Specimen sealed on card		£1.00

27.3 mm • 8.0 grammes • cupro-nickel • plain edge

COMMEMORATIVE TYPE 23 (Olympic 7)
50 PENCE
Boxing Gloves with Ring Ropes
(London 2012 Olympics - Boxing)
Design by: Shane Abery
Obverse: 4

		UNC	BU
2011	805,000	FV	£1.00
	Specimen sealed on card		£1.50

COMMEMORATIVE TYPE 24 (Olympic 8)
50 PENCE
Canoeist in Choppy Waters
(London 2012 Olympics - Canoeing)
Design by: Timothy Lees
Obverse: 4

		UNC	BU
2011	1,010,000	FV	£1.00
	Specimen sealed on card		£2.00

COMMEMORATIVE TYPE 25 (Olympic 9)
50 PENCE
Cyclist
(London 2012 Olympics - Cycling)
Design by: Theo Crutchley-Mack
Obverse: 4

		UNC	BU
2011	800,000	FV	£0.75
	Specimen sealed on card		£1.00
	.925 Silver Proof - See note, page 59		£20.00

COMMEMORATIVE TYPE 26 (Olympic 10)
50 PENCE
Horse, Jumping
(London 2012 Olympics - Equestrian)
Design by: Thomas Babbage
Obverse: 4

		UNC	BU
2011	1,005,000	FV	£1.00
	Specimen sealed on card		£1.50

COMMEMORATIVE TYPE 27 (Olympic 11)
50 PENCE
Fencing
(London 2012 Olympics - Fencing)
Design by: Ruth Summerfield
Obverse: 4

		UNC	BU
2011	1,005,000	£1.00	£1.50
	Specimen sealed on card		£2.00

COMMEMORATIVE TYPE 28 (Olympic 12)
OFFSIDE EXPLAINED / 50 PENCE
Diagram of the Offside Rule
(London 2012 Olympics - Football)
Design by: Neil Wolfson
Obverse: 4

		UNC	BU
2011	500,000	FV	£1.00
	Specimen sealed on card		£2.00

COMMEMORATIVE TYPE 29 (Olympic 13)
50 PENCE
Player with Ball
(London 2012 Olympics - Goalball)
Design by: Jonathan Wren
Obverse: 4

		UNC	BU
2011	1,005,000	£1.00	£1.50
	Specimen sealed on card		£2.00

COMMEMORATIVE TYPE 30 (Olympic 14)
50 PENCE
Gymnast
(London 2012 Olympics - Gymnastics)
Design by: Jonathan Olliffe
Obverse: 4

		UNC	BU
2011	1,007,313	FV	£1.00
	Specimen sealed on card		£1.50

COMMEMORATIVE TYPE 31 (Olympic 15)
50 PENCE
Player with Ball
(London 2012 Olympics - Handball)
Design by: Natasha Ratcliffe
Obverse: 4

		UNC	BU
2011	1,005,000	FV	£2.00
	Specimen sealed on card		£3.00

COMMEMORATIVE TYPE 32 (Olympic 16)
50 PENCE
Two Hockey Players
(London 2012 Olympics - Hockey)
Design by: Robert Evans
Obverse: 4

		UNC	BU
2011	1,001,000	£0.80	£1.50
	Specimen sealed on card		£2.00

COMMEMORATIVE TYPE 33 (Olympic 17)
50 PENCE
Judo Throw
(London 2012 Olympics - Judo)
Design by: David Cornell
Obverse: 4

		UNC	BU
2011	1,005,000	£2.00	£3.00
	Specimen sealed on card		£4.00

COMMEMORATIVE TYPE 34 (Olympic 18)
50 PENCE
Swimmer and four Silhouettes
(London 2012 Olympics - Modern Pentathlon)
Design by: Daniel Brittain
Obverse: 4

		UNC	BU
2011	705,000	FV	£1.00
	Specimen sealed on card		£2.00

27.3 mm • 8.0 grammes • cupro-nickel • plain edge

COMMEMORATIVE TYPE 35 (Olympic 19)
50 PENCE
Slogans and Two Rowers
(London 2012 Olympics - Rowing)
Design by: Davey Podmore
Obverse: 4

		UNC	BU
2011	1,005,300	FV	£1.00
	Specimen sealed on card		£1.50

COMMEMORATIVE TYPE 36 (Olympic 20)
50 PENCE
Sailing Boats on the Sea
(London 2012 Olympics - Sailing)
Design by: Bruce Rushin
Obverse: 4

		UNC	BU
2011	1,005,000	FV	£1.00
	Specimen sealed on card		£1.50

COMMEMORATIVE TYPE 37 (Olympic 21)
50 PENCE
Figure, Shooting
(London 2012 Olympics - Shooting)
Design by: Pravin Dewdhory
Obverse: 4

		UNC	BU
2011	1,005,000	£1.00	£1.50
	Specimen sealed on card		£2.00

COMMEMORATIVE TYPE 38 (Olympic 22)
50 PENCE
Table Tennis Bats, Ball etc
(London 2012 Olympics - Table Tennis)
Design by: Alan Linsdell
Obverse: 4

		UNC	BU
2011	1,010,000	FV	£1.00
	Specimen sealed on card		£1.50

COMMEMORATIVE TYPE 39 (Olympic 23)
50 PENCE
Two Figures Participating in Taekwando
(London 2012 Olympics - Taekwando)
Design by: David Gibbons
Obverse: 4

		UNC	BU
2011	1,664,000	£1.00	£2.00
	Specimen sealed on card		£3.00

COMMEMORATIVE TYPE 40 (Olympic 24)
50 PENCE
Tennis Ball and Net
(London 2012 Olympics - Tennis)
Design by: Tracy Baines
Obverse: 4

		UNC	BU
2011	605,000	FV	£2.00
	Specimen sealed on card		£2.50

27.3 mm • 8.0 grammes • cupro-nickel • plain edge

COMMEMORATIVE TYPE 41 (Olympic 25)
50 PENCE
Silhouettes of Runner, Cyclist and Swimmer
(London 2012 Olympics - Triathlon)
Design by: Sarah Harvey
Obverse: 4

		UNC	BU
2011	1,011,000	£5.00	£6.00
	Specimen sealed on card		£8.00

COMMEMORATIVE TYPE 42 (Olympic 26)
50 PENCE
Three Players and Central Net
(London 2012 Olympics - Volleyball)
Design by: Daniela Boothman
Obverse: 4

		UNC	BU
2011	1,005,000	FV	£1.00
	Specimen sealed on card		£1.50

COMMEMORATIVE TYPE 43 (Olympic 27)
50 PENCE
Basic Outline of a Weightlifter
(London 2012 Olympics - Weightlifting)
Design by: Rob Shakespeare
Obverse: 4

		UNC	BU
2011	1,105,000	£1.00	£1.50
	Specimen sealed on card		£2.00

COMMEMORATIVE TYPE 44 (Olympic 28)
50 PENCE
Man Playing, Ball in Lap
(London 2012 Olympics - Wheelchair Rugby)
Design by: Natasha Ratcliffe
Obverse: 4

		UNC	BU
2011	505,000	FV	£1.00
	Specimen sealed on card		£1.50
	.925 Silver Proof - See note, page 59		£20.00

COMMEMORATIVE TYPE 45 (Olympic 29)
50 PENCE
Wrestlers
(London 2012 Olympics - Wrestling)
Design by: Roderick Enriquez
Obverse: 4

		UNC	BU
2011	505,000	FV	£1.00
	Specimen sealed on card		£2.00

Olympic 30
Medallion Only
The Royal Mint issued a medallion with the 29x 50p coins. It's not a coin, but is mentioned here for completeness. Values are around £10.

The 50p Olympic Coins - Silver Proofs?

Noted so far in silver proof form are: Basketball, Cycling and Wheelchair Rugby. The Royal Mint apparently also made three 'sets' of six silver proof coins which included the Fencing, Badminton, Basketball, Hockey, Tennis and the, I quote, 'wildly popular' football coin!

FIFTY PENCE / 50
Ironside's rejected design for the original 50p
(This is what the original 50p could have looked like)
Design by: Christopher Ironside
Obverse: 4

	UNC	BU	Proof
2013	£1.00	£3.00	£10.00
Specimen in folder, price new		£8.00	
.925 sterling silver proof, price new			£45.00
.925 sterling silver piedfort proof, price new			£90.00
.917 gold proof, price new			£700.00

BENJAMIN / COMPOSER BORN 1913 / BRITTEN
His name in a double stave,
'Blow Bugle blow' and 'Set the
wild echoes flying'.
(To mark the centenary of the birth
of Benjamin Britten)
Design by: Tom Phillips

	UNC	BU	Proof
2013	£1.00	£3.00	£10.00
Specimen in folder		£9.00	
.925 sterling silver proof, price new			£45.00
.925 sterling silver piedfort proof, price new			£90.00
.917 gold proof, price new			£700.00

XX / COMMONWEALTH GAMES GLASGOW / 2014
Male cyclist and female runner
(To commemorate the 20th Commonwealth
Games)
Design by: Alex Loudon and Dan Flashman

	UNC	BU	Proof
2014	£1.00	£4.00	£15.00
Specimen in folder, price new		£10.00	

ROTOGRAPHIC

Specialist publishers of price guide reference books. Established 1959

Collectors' Coins GB 2014

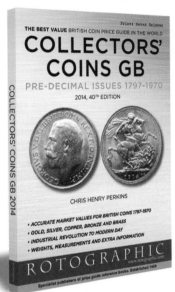

The 40th annual edition of the world's best-value British coin price guide.

This all-new version includes valuations and comprehensive data for all British coins since the Industrial Revolution, up to the end of the 'old' pre-decimal money.

ISBN (printed edition): 978-0-948964-09-1. RRP £7.35

ISBN (eBook edition): 978-0-901170-21-7. RRP £4.40

Available from all good book retailers.

Features include:
- Market values for gold, silver and base metal coins 1797 to 1968.
- Huge amounts of information about sizes, weights & designers.
- Previously unpublished varieties are listed.

What's currently legal tender?

All £1 coins are legal tender. The £1 coin is the most commonly forged coin, with estimates of between 1-2% of the total £1 coins in circulation being forgeries. Look out for poor definition and mis-matching edges or reverses (i.e a Welsh reverse with a date that should have an English obverse, and/or a coin with edge lettering that doesn't match the country represented on its reverse). If someone gives you a fake £1 coin, you are not legally obliged to accept it.

Which are hard to find?

The hardest £1 coin to be found in circulation is 1988. A relatively low mintage of just over seven million doesn't make it rare, but it's certainly the scarcest in comparison to the others.

OBVERSE

OBVERSE 1
(used 1983 - 1984)
D•G•REG•F•D•(date) || ELIZABETH II
Elizabeth II, Dei Gratia Regina, Fidei Defensor
(Elizabeth II, By the Grace of God Queen and Defender of the Faith)
Portrait by: Arnold Machin

OBVERSE 2
(used 1985 - 1997)
ELIZABETH II || D•G•REG•F•D•(date)
Elizabeth II, Dei Gratia Regina, Fidei Defensor
(Elizabeth II, By the Grace of God Queen and Defender of the Faith)
Portrait by: Raphael Maklouf

OBVERSE 3
(used 1998 - 2008)
ELIZABETH II•D•G || REG•F•D•(date)
Elizabeth II, Dei Gratia Regina, Fidei Defensor
(Elizabeth II, By the Grace of God Queen and Defender of the Faith)
Portrait by: Ian Rank-Broadley

OBVERSE 4 (similar to last, with no rim beading)
(used 2008 to date)
ELIZABETH II•D•G || REG•F•D•(date)
Elizabeth II, Dei Gratia Regina, Fidei Defensor
(Elizabeth II, By the Grace of God Queen and Defender of the Faith)
Portrait by: Ian Rank-Broadley

1983   UK Royal Arms design by Eric Sewell

		UNC	BU	Proof
443,053,510		£1.50	£2.00	£5.00
484,900	Specimen in folder		£2.50	
50,000	.925 sterling silver proof			£25.00
10,000	.925 sterling silver piedfort proof			£115.00

The following 4 coins ("Coronet" series) were designed by Leslie Durban.

1984   Scottish Thistle in Coronet

146,256,501		£1.50	£2.00	£5.00
27,960	Specimen in folder		£2.50	
44,855	.925 sterling silver proof			£20.00
15,000	.925 sterling silver piedfort proof			£30.00

1985   Welsh Leek in Coronet

228,430,749		£1.50	£2.00	£5.00
24,850	Specimen in folder		£2.50	
50,000	.925 sterling silver proof			£20.00
15,000	.925 sterling silver piedfort proof			£30.00

1986   N.I. Flax in Coronet

10,409,501		£1.50	£2.00	£5.00
19,908	Specimen in folder		£2.50	
37,958	.925 sterling silver proof			£20.00
15,000	.925 sterling silver piedfort proof			£30.00

1987   English Oak in Coronet

39,298,50		£1.50	£2.00	£5.00
72,607	Specimen in folder		£2.50	
50,500	.925 sterling silver proof			£20.00
15,000	.925 sterling silver piedfort proof			£30.00

22.5 mm • 9.5 grammes • nickel-brass • lettered edge

1988   Royal Shield design (UK) by Derek Gorringe

		UNC	BU	Proof
7,118,825		£2.00	£3.00	£5.00
29,550	Specimen in folder		£5.00	
50,000	.925 sterling silver proof			£25.00
10,000	.925 sterling silver piedfort proof			£30.00

The following 4 coins ("Coronet" series) were designed by Leslie Durban.

1989   Scottish Thistle in Coronet

70,580,501		£1.50	£2.00	£5.00
25,000	.925 sterling silver proof			£20.00
10,000	.925 sterling silver piedfort proof			£30.00

1990   Welsh Leek in Coronet

97,269,302		£1.50	£2.00	£5.00
25,000	.925 sterling silver proof			£20.00
10,000	.925 sterling silver piedfort proof			£30.00

1991   N.I. Flax in Coronet

38,443,575		£1.50	£2.00	
25,000	.925 sterling silver proof			
10,000	.925 sterling silver piedfort proof			

1992   English Oak in Coronet

36,320,487				
25,000	.925 sterling silver proof			
10,000	.925 sterling silver piedfort proof			

19 June 1999

1993   UK Royal Arms design by Eric Sewell

	UNC	BU	Proof
114,744,500	£1.50	£2.00	£5.00
484,900 Specimen in folder		£2.510	
50,000 .925 sterling silver proof			£20.00
10,000 .925 sterling silver piedfort proof			£30.00

The following 4 coins ("Heraldic" series) were designed by Norman Sillman.

1994   Scottish Lion Rampant

	UNC	BU	Proof
29,752,525	£1.50	£2.00	£5.00
Specimen in folder		£2.50	
25,000 .925 sterling silver proof			£20.00
11,722 .925 sterling silver piedfort proof			£30.00

1995   Welsh Dragon

	UNC	BU	Proof
34,503,501	£1.50	£2.00	£5.00
Specimen in folder		£2.50	
Specimen in folder (Welsh text)		£8.00	
27,445 .925 sterling silver proof			£20.00
8,458 .925 sterling silver piedfort proof			£30.00

1996   N.I. Celtic Cross

	UNC	BU	Proof
89,886,000	£1.50	£2.00	£5.00
Specimen in folder		£2.50	
25,000 .925 sterling silver cased proof			£20.00
10,000 .925 sterling silver piedfort cased proof			£30.00

1997   English Three Lions

	UNC	BU	Proof
57,117,450	£1.50	£2.00	£5.00
Specimen in folder		£2.50	
20,137 .925 sterling silver proof			£20.00
10,000 .925 sterling silver piedfort proof			£30.00

22.5 mm • 9.5 grammes • nickel-brass • lettered edge

1998	UK Royal Arms design by Eric Sewell			
		UNC	BU	Proof
(BU sets only)			£10.00	£10.00
13,843	.925 sterling silver proof			£25.00
10,000	.925 sterling silver piedfort proof			£35.00

1999	Scottish Lion Rampant			
(BU sets only)			£10.00	£10.00
25,000	.925 sterling silver proof			£25.00
2,000	.925 sterling "Special Frosted Finish" proof			£35.00
10,000	.925 sterling silver piedfort proof			£35.00

2000	Welsh Dragon			
109,496,500		£1.50	£2.50	£5.00
40,000	.925 sterling silver proof			£25.00
2,000	.925 sterling "Special Frosted Finish" proof			£35.00
10,000	.925 sterling silver piedfort proof			£35.00

2001	N.I. Celtic Cross			
58,093,731		£1.50	£2.50	£5.00
13,237	.925 sterling silver proof			£25.00
2,000	.925 sterling "Special Frosted Finish" proof			£35.00
8,464	.925 sterling silver piedfort proof			£35.00

2002	English Three Lions			
77,818,000		£1.50	£2.50	£5.00
17,693	.925 sterling silver proof			£25.00
2,000	.925 sterling "Special Frosted Finish" proof			£35.00
6,599	.925 sterling silver piedfort proof			£35.00

2003	UK Royal Arms design by Eric Sewell			
61,596,500		£1.50	£2.50	£5.00
15,830	.925 sterling silver proof			£25.00
9,871	.925 sterling silver piedfort proof			£35.00

The following 4 coins ("Bridge" series) were designed by Edwina Ellis.

2004　Scotland - Forth Bridge

		UNC	BU	Proof
39,162,000		£1.50	£2.00	£5.00
24,014	Specimen in folder		£3.00	
11,470	.925 sterling silver proof			£25.00
7,013	.925 sterling silver piedfort cased proof			£35.00
2,618	.917 gold proof			£500.00

2005　Wales - Menai Bridge

99,429,500		£1.50	£2.00	£5.00
24,802	Specimen in folder		£3.00	
8,371	.925 sterling silver proof			£25.00
6,007	.925 sterling silver piedfort cased proof			£40.00
1,195	.917 gold proof			£500.00

2006　Northern Ireland - Egyptian Arch

38,938,000		£1.40	£2.00	£5.00
23,856	Specimen in folder		£3.00	
14,765	.925 sterling silver proof			£28.00
5,129	.925 sterling silver piedfort cased proof			£40.00
728	.917 gold proof			£550.00

2007　England - Millenium Bridge

26,180,160		£1.00	£2.00	£5.00
5,326	Specimen in folder		£5.00	
10,110	.925 sterling silver proof			£28.00
5,739	.925 sterling silver piedfort cased proof			£40.00
1,122	.917 gold proof			£550.00

1983 to 2008 UK, English and NI reverse designs and also the 2008 onwards shield reverse type carry the edge inscription:

DECUS ET TUTAMEN (An ornament and a safeguard)

1984 to 1999 Scottish reverse designs carry the edge inscription:

NEMO ME IMPUNE LACESSIT (No-one provokes me with impunity)

1985 to 2000 Welsh reverse designs carry the edge inscription:

PLEIDIOL WYF I'M GWLAD (True am I to my country)

65

2008   UK Royal Arms design by: Eric Sewell. With Obverse 3.

		UNC	BU	Proof
3,910,000		£1.50	£2.00	£6.00
9,134	.925 sterling silver proof			£30.00
7,894	.925 sterling silver piedfort cased proof			£45.00
2,005	Set of 14 £1 coins, all designs 1983 - 2008. Silver with gold coloured 'silhouette' details. All dated 2008			£450.00
	As above, as gold proof set			-

Large shield part of the UK Royal coat of Arms by: Matthew Dent. With Obverse 4. Struck annually.

2008	43,827,300	FV	£2.00	£8.00
5,000	.925 sterling silver proof			£30.00
2,456	.925 sterling piedfort proof			£50.00
860	.917 gold proof			£600.00

2009

	27,625,600	FV	£2.00	£8.00
	.925 sterling silver proof from set			£30.00
	.22ct Gold proof			£600.00

2010

	25,415,000	FV	£2.00	£8.00

2011

	35,700,030	FV	£2.00	£8.00

2012

	-	FV	£2.00	£8.00

2013

		FV	£2.00	£8.00
	.925 sterling silver proof			£50.00

2014

		FV	£2.00	£8.00

2010   Capital cities of the UK series - Belfast, by Stuart Devlin
        Edge: PRO TANTO QUID RETRIBUAMUS

	UNC	BU	Proof
6,205,000	FV	£2.00	£7.00
.925 sterling silver proof			£40.00
.925 sterling silver piedfort proof			£80.00

2010   Capital cities of the UK series - London, by Stuart Devlin
        Edge: DOMINE DIRIGE NOS

2,635,000	FV	£2.00	£7.00
.925 sterling silver proof			£40.00
.925 sterling silver piedfort proof			£80.00

2011   Capital cities of the UK series - Cardiff, by Stuart Devlin
        Edge: Y DDRAIS GOCH DDYRY CYCHWYN

1,615,000	FV	£2.00	£7.00
.925 sterling silver proof			£40.00
.925 sterling silver piedfort proof			£80.00

2011   Capital cities of the UK series - Edinburgh, by Stuart Devlin
        Edge: NISI DOMINUS FRUSTRA

935,000	FV	£2.00	£7.00
.925 sterling silver proof			£40.00
.925 sterling silver piedfort proof			£80.00

2013   National Floral Symbols series - England, by Timothy Noad
Edge: DECUS ET TUTAMEN

	UNC	BU	Proof
FV	£2.00	£5.00	£10.00
.925 sterling silver proof			£50.00
.925 sterling silver piedfort proof			£100.00

2013   National Floral Symbols series - Wales by Timothy Noad
Edge: PLEIDIOL WYF I'M GWLAD

	UNC	BU	Proof
FV	£2.00	£5.00	£10.00
.925 sterling silver proof			
.925 sterling silver piedfort proof			£50.00

? 2013 Silver proof version of the 1988 design   £100.00
? 2013 Silver proof version of the 1983 design   £100

2014   National Floral Symbols series - Scotland, by Timothy Noad
Edge: NEMO ME IMPUNE LACESSIT

FV	£2.00	£10.00	
.925 sterling silver proof			
.925 sterling silver piedfort proof		£100.00	

2014   National Floral Symbols series - N. Ireland, by Timothy Noad
Edge: DECUS ET TUTAMEN

FV	£2.00	£5.00	
.925 sterling silver proof			
.925 sterling silver piedfort proof		£100.00	

What's currently legal tender?

All £2 coins dated from 1986 to date are legal tender. The earlier single metal type coins dated 1986 to 1996 are not often seen in circulation and therefore may not be accepted by some merchants who are unfamiliar with them.

Which are hard to find?

All of the 1986 to 1996 (single alloy) £2 coins are now hard to find in circulation. The scarcest £2 coin is probably COMMEMORATIVE TYPE 3, the 'Claim of Right' coin, as this was minted in much smaller quantities than the other 1989 £2 coin, and was only issued in Scotland. The bi-metallic coin with the 'Queen wearing a necklace' was never rare, despite the fact that some did sell for more than face value in the late 90s because people hoarded them thinking they were scarce, and this actually did cause them to be scarce, albeit temporarily!

COMMEMORATIVE TYPE 1

A thistle encircled by a laurel wreath, superimposed on St. Andrew's Cross
(1986 Commonwealth Games, Edinburgh)
Reverse design by: Norman Sillman
Edge: XIII COMMONWEALTH GAMES SCOTLAND 1986

			UNC	BU	Proof
1986	8,212,184	104,591 Proofs	£3.00	£7.50	£10.00
		Specimen in folder		£8.00	
	58,881	.500 silver UNC	£15.00		
	59,779	.925 sterling silver proof			£22.00
		.917 gold proof			£450.00

COMMEMORATIVE TYPE 2

Intertwined W & M (monogrammes of William & Mary)
House of Commons Mace, English Crown
TERCENTENARY of the BILL of RIGHTS
1689-1989
Design by: John Lobban
Edge: MILLED

			UNC	BU	Proof
1989	4,777,891 Inc T3	84,704 Proofs	£3.00	£10.00	£15.00
		Partially non frosted proof*			£18.00
		Specimen in folder		£11.00	
	25,000	.925 sterling silver proof			£22.00
	10,000	.925 sterling silver, piedfort proof			£30.00

*Proofs that were part of a Bass Charington promotion appear to have a non frosted bust of the Queen. More comparison is needed at this stage.

COMMEMORATIVE TYPE 3
Intertwined W & M
(monogram of William & Mary)
House of Commons Mace, Scottish Crown
TERCENTENARY of the CLAIM of RIGHT
1689-1989
Design by: John Lobban
Edge: MILLED

			UNC	BU	Proof
1989	Inc. with T2	84,704 Proofs	£6.00	£10.00	£15.00
		Specimen in folder		£12.00	
	Specimen folder, including both versions ('Bill' & 'Claim')		£20.00		
	24,852	.925 sterling silver proof			£22.00
	10,000	.925 sterling silver, Piedfort proof			£30.00

COMMEMORATIVE TYPE 4
Intertwined W & M
(monogram of William & Mary)
Britannia Seated
BANK of ENGLAND 1694-1994
Design by: Leslie Durban
Edge: SIC VOS NON VOBIS

			UNC	BU	Proof
1994	1,443,116	67,721 Proofs	£3.00	£7.50	£10.00
		Specimen in folder		£9.00	
	27,957	.925 sterling silver proof			£22.00
	9,569	.925 sterling silver, Piedfort proof			£30.00
	1,000	.917 gold proof			£500.00
	Not known	Gold proof mule with wrong obverse*			£1700.00

*The obverse of the double sovereign type £2 coin was used in error. The Queen's head is larger, it breaks the more abbreviated legend at the top and the words 'TWO POUNDS' are not present.

COMMEMORATIVE TYPE 5
Dove of Peace
(Commemorating 50 years' peace,
since the end of World War II)
Reverse design by: John Mills
Edge: 1945 IN PEACE GOODWILL 1995

			UNC	BU	Proof
1995	4,388,006	60,639 Proofs	£3.00	£7.50	£10.00
		Specimen in folder		£9.00	
	50,000	.925 sterling silver proof			£22.00
	10,000	.925 sterling silver, Piedfort proof			£30.00
	2,500	.917 gold proof			£500.00

COMMEMORATIVE TYPE 6
UN logo, array of flags
NATIONS UNITED FOR PEACE 1945 - 1995
(50th Anniversary - United Nations)
Design by: Michael Rizzello
Edge: PLAIN MILLED

			UNC	BU	Proof
1995	Inc. with T5		£3.00	£7.50	£10.00
		Specimen in folder		£9.00	
	175,000	.925 sterling silver proof			£25.00
	10,000	.925 sterling silver Piedfort proof			£30.00
	2,098	.917 gold proof			£500.00

COMMEMORATIVE TYPE 7
Football design, with date, 1996, in centre
(10th European Championship)
Design by: John Mills
Edge: TENTH EUROPEAN CHAMPIONSHIP

			UNC	BU	Proof
1996	5,141,350		£3.00	£7.50	£10.00
	84,704	Specimen in folder		£9.00	
	50,000	.925 sterling silver proof			£20.00
	10,000	.925 sterling silver, Piedfort proof			£30.00
	2,098	.917 gold proof			£500.00

71

OBVERSE

OBVERSE 1
(used 1997 only)
ELIZABETH II DEI GRATIA REGINA F D
Elizabeth II, Dei Gratia Regina, Fidei Defensor
(Elizabeth II, By the Grace of God Queen and Defender of the Faith)
Portrait by: Raphael Maklouf

OBVERSE 2
(used 1998 to date on all coins with Reverse 1.
Also used on commemoratives 8 to 17, 19 and 32)
ELIZABETH II DEI GRATIA REGINA FID DEF
Elizabeth II, Dei Gratia Regina, Fidei Defensor
(Elizabeth II, By the Grace of God Queen and Defender of the Faith)
Portrait by: Ian Rank-Broadley

| OBVERSE 2b | OBVERSE 2c | OBVERSE 2d |

Variations of obverse 2 - Some of the later reverse designs don't include a date, the face value or both, so these have been incorporated into the obverse legend.

2b 'TWO POUNDS' at bottom - was used for Commemorative Types 18, 20, 24, 28, 29, 30 and 31
2c DATE at bottom - was used for Commemorative Types 21, 22, 23 and 25
2d 'TWO POUNDS' and DATE at bottom - was used for Commemorative Types 26 and 27

REVERSE

REVERSE 1 (the standard non-commemorative reverse)
(used 1997 to date)
Rings, representing stages of development:
from centre, outward: IRON AGE, INDUSTRIAL REVOLUTION
(cogs), ELECTRONIC AGE (silicon chips), INTERNET AGE
Edge: STANDING ON THE SHOULDERS OF GIANTS
Design by: Bruce Rushin

TRIAL TYPES
Sailing ship, probably representing the Golden Hind

A first Bi-metallic coin trial. Coins are dated 1994 but were actually released in 1998. The coins were all issued in packs which also contain examples of the outer and inner blanks and a nickel-brass ring. The obverse used is a modified OBVERSE 1 - very similar, but the trial obverse actually has a dot instead of a small cross between the 'D' and 'ELIZABETH'. The obverse lettering also appears weaker and slightly thinner than usual.

Edge: DECUS ET TUTAMEN ANNO REGNI XLVI
Value: The bi-metallic pack tends to sell for between £60 and £80.

Single metal £2 trial, dated 1994 and marked 'ROYAL MINT TRIAL' on both sides, also featuring the ship design.
These are very rare. **Value £500.00 - £2000.00**

TYPE 1 (obverse 1, reverse 1)

		UNC	BU	Proof
1997	13,734,625	£3.00	£4.00	£7.50
	Specimen in folder		£9.00	
29,910	.925 silver proof			£20.00
10,000	.925 silver piedfort proof			£40.00
2,482	.917 gold proof			£450.00

TYPE 2 (obverse 2, reverse 1)

			UNC	BU	Proof
1998	91,110,375	100,000	FV	£4.00	£7.50
1999*	38,652,000		£40.00	?£100.00?	
2000	25,770,000		FV	£4.00	£7.50
2001	34,984,750		FV	£4.00	£7.50
2002	13,024,750		FV	£4.00	£7.50
2003	17,531,250		FV	£4.00	£7.50
2004	11,981,500		FV	£4.00	£7.50
2005	3,837,250		FV	£4.00	£7.50
2006	16,715,000		FV	£4.00	£7.50
2007	10,270,000		FV	£4.00	£7.50
2008	30,107,000		FV	£4.00	£7.50
2009	8,775,000		FV	£4.00	£7.50
2010	6,890,000		FV	£4.00	£7.50
2011	24,375,030		FV	£4.00	£7.50
2012	3,900,000		FV	£4.00	£7.50
2013			FV	£10.00	£15.00
2014			FV	£10.00	£15.00

* 1999 was not issued as a proof or in BU sets and is therefore scarce to almost unheard of in top condition, despite the high mintage.

73

28.40 mm • 12.0 grammes • bi-metal • various edge

COMMEMORATIVE TYPE 8
Symbolic representation of a stadium with rugby
ball and goalposts. '1999' above, 'TWO POUNDS' below
(1999 Rugby World Cup)
Design by: Ron Dutton
Edge: RUGBY WORLD CUP 1999

			UNC	BU	Proof
1999	4,933,000		£3.00	£7.50	£10.00
		Specimen in folder		£9.00	
	9,665	.925 sterling silver proof			£22.00
	10,000	.925 sterling silver hologram Piedfort proof			£75.00
	311	.917 gold proof			£450.00

COMMEMORATIVE TYPE 9
Symbolic representation of Marconi's successful
transatlantic wireless transmission of 1901,
'TWO POUNDS' below
Design by: Robert Evans
Edge: WIRELESS BRIDGES THE ATLANTIC...MARCONI 1901...

			UNC	BU	Proof
2001	4,558,000		£3.00	£7.50	£10.00
		Specimen in folder		£9.00	
	11,488	.925 sterling silver proof			£22.00
	6,759	.925 sterling silver Piedfort proof			£40.00
	1,658	.917 gold proof			£450.00

COMMEMORATIVE TYPE 10
XVII COMMONWEALTH GAMES 2002
around athlete holding banner, (1 of 4) national flags
(27th Commonwealth Games, Manchester)
Design by: Matthew Bonaccorsi
Edge: SPIRIT OF FRIENDSHIP MANCHESTER 2002

			UNC	BU	Proof
2002	650,500	10-a English flag	£5.00	£10.00	£25.00
	485,500	10-b N. Ireland flag	£5.00	£10.00	£25.00
	771,750	10-c Scottish flag	£5.00	£10.00	£25.00
	588,500	10-d Welsh flag	£5.00	£10.00	£25.00

Sets of the 4 coins:

		Specimens in folder	£50.00
	47,895	base metal proof set	£100.00
	2,553	.925 sterling silver proof set	£200.00
	3,497	.925 sterling silver Piedfort set (coloured flags)	£250.00
	315	.917 gold proof set	£1,800.00

COMMEMORATIVE TYPE 11
DNA Double Helix pattern, DNA DOUBLE HELIX,
1953 TWO POUNDS 2003
(50th Anniversary - Discovery of DNA)
Design by: John Mills
Edge: DEOXYRIBONUCLEIC ACID

			UNC	BU	Proof
2003	4,299,000		£3.00	£7.50	£10.00
	41,568	Specimen in folder		£9.00	
	11,204	.925 sterling silver proof			£30.00
	8,728	.925 sterling silver Piedfort proof			£50.00
	1,500	.917 gold proof			£500.00

75

28.40 mm • 12.0 grammes • bi-metal • various edge

COMMEMORATIVE TYPE 12
Steam locomotive TWO POUNDS R.TREVITHICK
1804 INVENTION INDUSTRY PROGRESS 2004
(200th anniversary - Steam Locomotive)
Design by: Robert Lowe
Edge: pattern of arcs & curves, representing viaducts

			UNC	BU	Proof
2004	5,004,500		£3.00	£7.50	£10.00
	56,871	Specimen in folder		£9.00	
	10,233 of 25k	.925 sterling silver proof			£22.00
	5,303 of 10k	.925 sterling silver Piedfort cased proof			£40.00
	1,500	.917 gold proof			£500.00

COMMEMORATIVE TYPE 13
Swords, Maces, Croziers in a starbust pattern,
1605-2005, TWO POUNDS
(400th anniversary - Gunpowder Plot)
Design by: Peter Forster
Edge: REMEMBER REMEMBER THE FIFTH OF NOVEMBER*

			UNC	BU	Proof
2005	5,140,500		£3.00	£7.50	£10.00
	47,895	Specimen in folder		£9.00	
	4,394	.925 sterling silver proof			£22.00
	4,584	.925 sterling silver Piedfort proof			£50.00
	914	.917 gold proof			£550.00

* These very often end up having missing tails on the 'R's of the edge lettering, so that they can in extreme cases read PEMEMBEP PEMEMBEP THE FIFTH OF NOVEMBEP. This problem with certain edge letters has also been noted on some other £2 and £1 coins. It makes them a little more interesting, but it is my opinion that such errors should have no real affect on the value, especially at such a young stage in a coins' life! I say should have no real influence on the value, but it seems it does have an affect on value, at least on eBay, where PEMEMBER coins in normal used condition seem to be exchanging hands for £10 and examples in UNC or near to UNC condition have been sold for £20 - £30. Judging by the number of them that is constantly available, I can't really see this slight error increasing much in the future - assuming of course that the media don't stir up a frenzy akin to the dateless 20p and recently the Kew Gardens 50p!

COMMEMORATIVE TYPE 14
St. Paul's Cathedral, floodlit with spotlights.
1945-2005, TWO POUNDS
(60th anniversary - End of World War II)
Design by: Robert Elderton
Edge: IN VICTORY: MAGNANIMITY, IN PEACE: GOODWILL

			UNC	BU	Proof
2005	10,191,000		£3.00	£10.00	
	53,686	Specimen in folder		£12.00	
	Specimen folder (including special edition medallion)			£20.00	
	21,734	.925 sterling silver proof			£25.00
	Not Known	*Error edge: REMEMBER REMEMBER THE FIFTH OF NOVEMBER .925 silver proof, as above			£400.00?
	4,798	.925 sterling silver Piedfort proof			£40.00
	2,924	.917 gold proof			£500.00

* The error edge 60th Anniversary of the End of WWII £2 coin has obviously ended up with the edge inscription of the other themed £2 coin struck that year to commemorate the gunpowder plot! The author has only been informed about one such coin and was lucky enough to have been given the opportunity to purchase it. There may be others, (see also Type 18) and the fact that the mint made this error with a proof coin may also indicate that normal 'business' struck coins might suffer from the same error. And what about the piedfort and/or gold proof versions? This is one of those discoveries that can make new coins interesting! I'd be interested to hear if any other readers come across another example of the error edge inscription coins. Update 2014: no others have been reported in over 4 years.

COMMEMORATIVE TYPE 15
Portrait of Isambard Kingdom Brunel in front of machinery
TWO POUNDS | 2006
(200th anniversary - Birth of Isambard Kingdom Brunel)
Design by: Rod Kelly
Edge: 1806-59 . ISAMBARD KINGDOM BRUNEL . ENGINEER

			UNC	BU	Proof
2006	7,928,250		£3.00	£7.50	£10.00
	54,564	Specimen in folder		£9.00	
	7,251 of 20k	.925 sterling silver proof			£25.00
	3,199 of 5k	.925 sterling silver Piedfort proof			£35.00
	1,071 of 1,500	.917 gold proof			£550.00

77

28.40 mm • 12.0 grammes • bi-metal • various edge

COMMEMORATIVE TYPE 16
Representation of the engineering achievements of I.K.Brunel,
2006 | BRUNEL | TWO POUNDS
(200th anniversary - Birth of Isambard Kingdom Brunel)
Design by: Robert Evans
Edge: SO MANY IRONS IN THE FIRE

			UNC	BU	Proof
2006	7,452,250		£3.00	£7.50	£10.00
	12,694	Specimen in folder		£9.00	
	5,375 of 20k	.925 sterling silver proof			£25.00
	Not Known	.925 sterling silver proof with no edge lettering			£300.00?
	3,018 of 5k	.925 sterling silver Piedfort proof			£35.00
	746 of 1,500	.917 gold proof			£500.00

COMMEMORATIVE TYPE 17
Jigsaw pieces of the English rose and Scotish thistle,
TWO | 2007 | POUNDS | 1707
(300th anniversary - Act of Union between England and Scotland)
Design by: Yvonne Holton
Edge: UNITED INTO ONE KINGDOM

			UNC	BU	Proof
2007	7,545,000		£3.00	£7.50	£10.00
	8,863	Specimen in folder		£9.00	
	8,310	.925 sterling silver proof			£25.00
	4,000	.925 sterling silver Piedfort proof			£40.00
	750	.917 gold proof			£500.00

COMMEMORATIVE TYPE 18
Five link chain with broken link as the nought in 1807,
AN ACT FOR THE ABOLITION OF THE SLAVE TRADE | 2007
(200th anniversary - Abolition of the British slave trade)
Design by: David Gentleman
Edge: AM I NOT A MAN AND A BROTHER
Obverse: 2b

			UNC	BU	Proof
2007	8,445,000	(no 'DG' initials)	£3.00	£7.50	£10.00*
	8,688	Specimen in folder ('DG' to right of chain)£14.00			
	7,095	.925 sterling silver proof ('DG' to right of chain)			£25.00
	3,990	.925 sterling silver Piedfort proof			£40.00
	1000	.917 gold proof			£500.00

* A proof version of this coin is known to exist with the 'THE 4TH OLYMPIAD LONDON
edge legend, obviously meant for Type 19. See also the note under Type 14.

COMMEMORATIVE TYPE 19
Running Track
LONDON OLYMPIC CENTENARY | 1908 | TWO POUNDS | 2008
(Centenary - 1908 London Olympics)
Design by: Thomas T Docherty
Edge: THE 4TH OLYMPIAD LONDON
Obverse: 2

		UNC	BU	Proof
2008	910,000	£3.00	£7.50	£10.00
	29,594 of 100k Specimen in folder		£12.00	
	6,841 of 20k .925 sterling silver proof			£25.00
	1,619 of 2,000 .925 sterling silver Piedfort proof			£45.00
	1,908 .917 gold proof			£500.00

COMMEMORATIVE TYPE 20
Olympic flag and two hands
BEIJING 2008 | LONDON 2012
(Olympic handover ceremony)
Design by: Royal Mint in House
Edge: I CALL UPON THE YOUTH OF THE WORLD
Obverse: 2b

		UNC	BU	Proof
2008	918,000	£5.00	£15.00	
	47,765 of 250k Specimen in folder		£18.00	
	30,000 .925 sterling silver proof			£40.00
	3,000 .925 sterling silver Piedfort proof			£50.00
	3,250 .917 gold proof			£500.00

COMMEMORATIVE TYPE 21
Darwin facing ape
1809 DARWIN 2009 | TWO POUNDS
(200th anniversay - birth of Charles Darwin)
Design by: Suzie Zamit
Edge: ON THE ORIGIN OF SPECIES 1859
Obverse: 2c

		UNC	BU	Proof
2009	3,903,000	£3.00	£7.50	£10.00
	Specimen in folder		£9.00	
	.925 sterling silver proof			£30.00
	.925 sterling silver Piedfort proof			£75.00
	.917 gold proof			£550.00

28.40 mm • 12.0 grammes • bi-metal • various edge

COMMEMORATIVE TYPE 22
Burns quote
1759 ROBERT BURNS 1796 | TWO POUNDS
(250 years anniversay - birth of Robert Burns)
Design by: Royal Mint in House
Edge: SHOULD AULD ACQUAINTANCE BE FORGOT
Obverse: 2c

			UNC	BU	Proof
2009	3,253,000		£3.00	£7.50	£10.00
		Specimen in folder		£9.00	
		.925 sterling silver proof			£25.00
		.925 sterling silver Piedfort proof			£50.00
		.917 gold proof			£500.00

COMMEMORATIVE TYPE 23
Nurses hands feeling for a pulse
1820 - FLORENCE NIGHTINGALE - 1910 | TWO POUNDS
(150 years of modern nursing and to the centenary of the
death of Florence Nightingale)
Design by: Gordon Summers
Edge: 150 YEARS OF NURSING
Obverse: 2c

			UNC	BU	Proof
2010	6,175,000		£3.00	£7.50	£10.00
		Specimen in folder		£9.00	
		.925 sterling silver proof			£25.00
		.925 sterling silver Piedfort proof			£80.00
		.917 gold proof			£550.00

COMMEMORATIVE TYPE 24
King James' Bible
KING JAMES BIBLE | 1611 - 2011
(400 years anniversay - King James' Bible)
Design by: Paul Stafford & Benjamin Wright
Edge: THE AUTHORISED VERSION
Obverse: 2b

			UNC	BU	Proof
2011	975,000		£3.00	£7.50	£10.00
		Specimen in folder		£10.00	
		.925 sterling silver proof			£25.00
		.925 sterling silver Piedfort proof			£45.00
		.917 gold proof			£900.00

COMMEMORATIVE TYPE 25
Mary Rose
THE MARY ROSE | TWO POUNDS
(Centenary - Mary Rose)
Design by: John Bergdahl
Edge: 1511 . YOUR NOBLEST SHIPPE .
Obverse: 2c

			UNC	BU	Proof
2011	1,040,000		£3.00	£7.50	£10.00
		Specimen in folder		£12.00	
		.925 sterling silver proof			£45.00
		.925 sterling silver Piedfort proof			£50.00
		.917 gold proof			£700.00

COMMEMORATIVE TYPE 26
Olympic Handover
LONDON 2012 | RIO 2016
(Olympic handover ceremony)
Design by: Jonathan Olliffe
Edge: I CALL UPON THE YOUTH OF THE WORLD
Obverse: 2d

			UNC	BU	Proof
2012	65,000 (plus 'several hundred thousands more'. Source: RM]		£5.00		£15.00
		Specimen in folder		£20.00	
		.925 sterling silver proof			£90.00
		.925 sterling silver Piedfort proof			£150.00
		.917 gold proof			?

COMMEMORATIVE TYPE 27
Charles Dickens
1812 CHARLES DICKENS 1870
(200th anniversay - birth of Charles Dickens)
Design by: Matthew Dent
Edge: SOMETHING WILL TURN UP
Obverse: 2d

			UNC	BU	Proof
2012	3,903,000		£3.00	£7.50	£10.00
		Specimen in folder		£10.00	
		.925 sterling silver proof			£35.00
		.925 sterling silver Piedfort proof			£55.00
		.917 gold proof			?

COMMEMORATIVE TYPE 28
Underground Roundal
1863 | UNDERGROUND | 2013
(150th anniversary - The London Underground)
Design by: Edwina Ellis
Edge: MIND THE GAP
Obverse: 2b

	UNC	BU	Proof
2013	£3.00	£10.00	£15.00
Specimen in folder		£20.00	
.925 sterling silver proof			£40.00
.925 sterling silver Piedfort proof			£80.00
.917 gold proof			?

COMMEMORATIVE TYPE 29
Underground Train
1863 | LONDON UNDERGROUND | 2013
(150th anniversary - The London Underground)
Design by: Edward Barber and Jay Osgerby
Edge: A pattern of circles connected by lines.
Obverse: 2b

	UNC	BU	Proof
2013	£3.00	£10.00	£15.00
Specimen in folder		£20.00	
.925 sterling silver proof			£40.00
.925 sterling silver Piedfort proof			£80.00
.917 gold proof			?

COMMEMORATIVE TYPE 30
Spade Guinea
ANIVERSARY OF THE GOLDEN GUINEA | 2013
(350th anniversary - the Guinea)
Design by: Anthony Smith
Edge: WHAT IS A GUINEA? 'TIS A SPLENDID THING
Obverse: 2b

	UNC	BU	Proof
2013	£3.00	£10.00	£15.00
Specimen in folder		£20.00	
.925 sterling silver proof, price new			£52.50
.925 sterling silver Piedfort proof			?
.917 gold proof			?

COMMEMORATIVE TYPE 31
Design from Kitchener recruitment poster
THE FIRST WORLD WAR 1914 - 1918 | 2014
(Centenary - Start of WWI)
Design by: John Bergdahl
Edge: THE LAMPS ARE GOING OUT ALL OVER EUROPE
Obverse: 2b

	UNC	BU	Proof
2014	£3.00	£10.00	£15.00
Specimen in folder, price new		£10.00	
.925 sterling silver proof			TBC
.925 sterling silver Piedfort proof			TBC
.917 gold proof			TBC

COMMEMORATIVE TYPE 32
Top of a Lighthouse
1514 TRINITY HOUSE 2014 | TWO POUNDS
(500 years of Trinity house)
Design by: Joe Whitlock Blundell and David Eccles
Edge: SERVING THE MARINER
Obverse 2

	UNC	BU	Proof
2014	£3.00	£10.00	£15.00
Specimen in folder, price new		£10.00	
.925 sterling silver proof			TBC
.925 sterling silver Piedfort proof			TBC
.917 gold proof			TBC

What's currently legal tender?

All £5 coins are legal tender. Look out for non UK £5 coins being offered for face value as these are often from smaller provinces/islands and are therefore not legal tender in the United Kingdom. Particularly worrying are the coins from Tristan da Cunha, a tiny island group with a population of less than 300. So-called £5 coins from Tristan da Cunha often look very British but simply have TDC in the legend. Earlier crown coins should not be confused with these post-1990 £5 crowns. The crowns struck from 1972 to 1981 have a face value of 25p.

Which are hard to find?

All of these large coins are hard to find in circulation because they tend to get hoarded by the public when they are new and they are also made in lower numbers than the lower denominations. They are also heavy and not really practical to carry around for day-to-day transactions. The COMMEMORATIVE TYPE 7 with the 2000 date on the obverse seems scarcer than the 1999 dated millenium coin.

COMMEMORATIVE TYPE 1
Standard portrait of QE II
Design by: Raphael Maklouf
Double "E" monogram, crowned
Design by: Leslie Durban

			UNC	BU	Proof
1990	2,761,431		£6.00	£7.00	£10.00
	Specimen in card/folder			£10.00	
	56,102	.925 sterling silver proof			£25.00
	2,750	.917 gold proof			£1300.00

COMMEMORATIVE TYPE 2
Mary Gillick portrait of QEII
design by: Robert Elderton
St. Edward's crown
Design by: Robert Elderton

			UNC	BU	Proof
1993	1,834,655		£6.00	£7.00	£10.00
	Specimen in folder			£9.00	
	75,000	.925 sterling silver proof			£25.00
	2,750	.917 gold proof			£1200.00

COMMEMORATIVE TYPE 3
Standard portrait of QE II
Design by: Raphael Maklouf
Windsor Castle and Pennants
Design by: Avril Vaughan
Edge:
VIVAT REGINA ELIZABETHA

			UNC	BU	Proof
1996	2,396,100		£6.00	£7.00	£10.00
		Specimen in folder		£9.00	
	75,000	.925 sterling silver proof			£25.00
	2,750	.917 gold proof			£1200.00

COMMEMORATIVE TYPE 4
Conjoined busts of Elizabeth II
and Prince Philip
Design by: Philip Nathan
**Arms of the Royal Couple,
crown, anchor.** Design by: Leslie
Durban

			UNC	BU	Proof
1997	1,733,000		£6.00	£7.00	£10.00
		Specimen in folder		£9.00	
	33,689	.925 sterling silver proof			£25.00
	2,750	.917 gold proof			£1200.00

COMMEMORATIVE TYPE 5
Standard portrait of QE II
Design by: Ian Rank-Broadley
Prince Charles, "The Prince's Trust"
Design by: Michael Noakes

			UNC	BU	Proof
1998	1,407,300	100,000	£5.50	£7.00	£10.00
		Specimen in folder		£9.00	
	35,000	.925 sterling silver proof			£25.00
	2,000	.917 gold proof			£1200.00

38.6l mm • 28.28 grammes • cupro-nickel • various edge

COMMEMORATIVE TYPE 6
Standard portrait of QEII
Design by: Ian Rank-Broadley
Portrait of Princess Diana
Design by: David Cornell

		UNC	BU	Proof
1999		£5.50	£7.00	£10.00
	Specimen in folder		£9.00	
49,545	.925 sterling silver proof			£25.00
2,750	.917 gold proof			£1200.00

COMMEMORATIVE TYPE 7
Standard portrait of QE II
(Dated either 1999 or 2000)
Design by: Ian Rank-Broadley
**Clock at midnight, with map
of British Isles**
Design by: Jeffrey Matthews
edge: WHAT'S PAST IS PROLOGUE

		UNC	BU	Proof
Dated 1999 on Obverse		£5.50	£7.00	£10.00
	Specimen in folder		£9.00	
75,000	.925 sterling silver cased proof			£25.00
2,750	.917 gold cased proof			£1200.00
Dated 2000 on Obverse (not shown)		£10.00	£15.00	£15.00
	Specimen in folder		£15.00	
75,000	.925 sterling silver proof			£40.00
2,750	.917 gold proof			£1200.00

COMMEMORATIVE TYPE 7a

Special dome mintmarked piece, available only at the Millennium Dome.

2000	Specimen in folder	£30.00

COMMEMORATIVE TYPE 8
Standard portrait of QE II
Design by: Ian Rank-Broadley
Portrait of the Queen Mother
Design by: Ian Rank-Broadley

		UNC	BU	Proof
2000		£5.50	£7.00	£10.00
	Specimen in folder		£9.00	
100,000	.925 sterling silver proof			£30.00
14,850	.925 sterling silver Piedfort proof			£65.00
2,750	.917 gold proof			£1200.00

COMMEMORATIVE TYPE 9
Standard portrait of QEII
Design by: Ian Rank-Broadley
Wyon portrait of Victoria
Design by: Mary Milner Dickens

		UNC	BU	Proof
2001	851,491	£6.00	£8.00	£10.00
	44,090 Specimen in folder		£11.00	
	19,812 .925 sterling silver proof			£30.00
	2,831 .917 gold proof			£1200.00

38.61 mm • 28.28 grammes • cupro-nickel • various edge

COMMEMORATIVE TYPE 10
Queen Elizabeth II on horseback
Design by: Ian Rank-Broadley
Queen wearing robes and diadem
Design by: Ian Rank-Broadley

		UNC	BU	Proof
2002		£5.50	£7.00	£10.00
340,230	Specimen in folder		£9.00	
54,012	.925 sterling silver proof			£30.00
3,461	.917 gold proof			£1200.00

COMMEMORATIVE TYPE 11
Standard portrait of QEII
Design by: Ian Rank-Broadley
Portrait of Queen Mother
Design by: Avril Vaughan. edge:
**STRENGTH DIGNITY
LAUGHTER**

		UNC	BU	Proof
2002		£5.50	£7.00	£10.00
	Specimen in folder		£9.00	
35,000	.925 sterling silver proof			£30.00
2,750	.917 gold proof			£1200.00

COMMEMORATIVE TYPE 12
Sketched portrait of QE II
Design by: Tom Philips
"GOD SAVE THE QUEEN"
Design by: Tom Philips

		UNC	BU	Proof
2003	1,307,010	£5.50	£7.00	£10.00
	Specimen in folder		£9.00	
75,000	.925 sterling silver proof			£30.00
3,500	.917 gold proof			£1200.00

COMMEMORATIVE TYPE 13
Standard portrait of QEII
Design by: Ian Rank-Broadley
Conjoined Britannia and Marianne
Design by: David Gentlemen

		UNC	BU	Proof
2004	1,205,594	£6.00	£8.00	£10.00
	11, 295 of 15k	.925 sterling silver proof		£30.00
	926 of 1,500	.917 gold proof		£1200.00
	501	.9995 platinum cased proof (3.0271 troy oz)		-

COMMEMORATIVE TYPE 14
Standard portrait of QE II
design by: Ian Rank-Broadley
Portrait of Horatio Nelson
design by: James Butler

		UNC	BU	Proof
2005	1,075,516 inc. Type 15	£5.50	£7.00	£10.00
	72,498	Specimen in folder	£11.00	
	12,852	.925 sterling silver proof		£30.00
	1,760	.917 gold proof		£1200.00

COMMEMORATIVE TYPE 15
Standard portrait of QEII
design by: Ian Rank-Broadley
HMS Victory & Temeraire
design by: Clive Duncan

		UNC	BU	Proof
2005	Inc. above, with Type 14	£5.50	£7.00	£10.00
	79,868	Specimen in folder	£11.00	
	Specimen set (contains both 2005 folders, in sleeve)	£25.00		
	21,448	.925 sterling silver proof		£30.00
	1,805	.917 gold proof		£1200.00

COMMEMORATIVE TYPE 16
Standard portrait of QEII
Design by: Ian Rank-Broadley
**Ceremonial Trumpets
with Banners**
Design by: Danuta Solowiej-Wedderburn

		UNC	BU	Proof
2006		£5.50	£7.00	£10.00
330,790	Specimen in folder		£9.00	
20,790 of 50k	.925 sterling silver proof			£30.00
5,000	.925 sterling silver piedfort proof			£80.00
2,750	.917 gold proof			£1200.00

COMMEMORATIVE TYPE 17
Standard portrait of QEII
Design by: Ian Rank-Broadley
**The North Rose Window at
Westminster Abbey**
Design by: Emma Noble

		UNC	BU	Proof
2007	2,396,100	£5.50	£7.00	£10.00
	260,856	Specimen in folder	£10.00	
	15,186 of 35k	.925 sterling silver proof		£40.00
	2,000 of 5,000	.925 sterling silver piedfort proof		£80.00
	2,380 of 2,500	.917 gold proof		£1200.00
	250	Platinum piedfort proof		£4000.00

COMMEMORATIVE TYPE 18
Standard portrait of QEII
Design by: Ian Rank-Broadley
Portrait of Elizabeth I
Westminster Abbey
Design by: Rod Kelly

			UNC	BU	Proof
2008			£5.50	£7.00	£10.00
		Specimen in folder		£10.00	
	9,216 of 20,000	.925 sterling silver proof			£40.00
	1,602 of 2,000	.925 sterling silver piedfort proof			£80.00
	1,500	.917 gold proof			£1200.00
	125 of 150	Platinum piedfort proof			£4000.00

COMMEMORATIVE TYPE 19
Standard portrait of QEII
Design by: Ian Rank-Broadley
Portrait of the Price of Wales
Design by: Ian Rank-Broadley

			UNC	BU	Proof
2008	30,649		£5.50	£7.00	£10.00
	54,746	Specimen in folder		£10.00	
	6,264	.925 sterling silver proof			£40.00
	1088 of 5000	.925 sterling silver piedfort proof			£80.00
	867 of 1500	.917 gold proof			£1200.00
	54 of 150	Platinum piedfort proof			£4000.00

COMMEMORATIVE TYPE 20
Standard portrait of QEII
Design by: Ian Rank-Broadley
Henry VIII
Design by: John Bergdahl

		UNC	BU	Proof
2009		£5.50	£7.00	£10.00
	Specimen in folder		£10.00	
20,000 max	.925 sterling silver proof			£40.00
4009 max	.925 sterling silver piedfort proof			£80.00
1509 max	.917 gold proof			£1200.00
100 max	Platinum piedfort proof			£4000.00

COMMEMORATIVE TYPE 21
Standard portrait of QEII
Design by: Ian Rank-Broadley
Countdown '3'
Design by: Claire Aldridge

		UNC	BU	Proof
2009		£5.50	£7.00	£10.00
	Specimen in folder		£10.00	
30,000 max	.925 sterling silver proof			£40.00
6000 max	.925 sterling silver piedfort proof			£80.00
4000 max	.917 gold proof			£1200.00

2009 - 2010 Best of Britain, 18 Crowns.

Dated 2009 and 2010 the Royal Mint issued a whopping 18 different crowns in conjunction with the London 2012 Olympics featuring Stonehenge, Winston Churchill, the Gower peninsula and other patriotic themes. The 18 coins were only available in silver proof guise. Designs were by Shane Greeves and at over £1000 per set, I have a feeling they probably didn't sell very many. I've not seen any for sale and there is no longer any information on the Royal Mint web site.

COMMEMORATIVE TYPE 22
Standard portrait of QEII
Design by: Ian Rank-Broadley
1660 Restoration of Monarchy
Design by: David Cornell
Obverse: Type as no. 20

		UNC	BU	Proof
2010		£5.50	£7.00	£10.00
	Specimen in folder		£10.00	
20,000 max	.925 sterling silver proof			£40.00
5,000 max	.925 sterling silver piedfort proof			£80.00
1200 max	.917 gold proof			£1200.00
100 max	Platinum piedfort proof			£4000.00

COMMEMORATIVE TYPE 23
Standard portrait of QEII
Design by: Ian Rank-Broadley
Countdown '2'
Design by: Claire Aldridge

		UNC	BU	Proof
2010		£5.50	£7.00	£10.00
	Specimen in folder		£10.00	
30,000 max	.925 sterling silver proof			£40.00
4000 max	.925 sterling silver piedfort proof			£80.00
3000 max	.917 gold proof			£1200.00

As part of the Royal Mints unprecedented drive to make as many themed coins as possible, higher face value coins were also issued. In silver: a £10 with a diameter of 65mm and weight of 5oz (155.5g) featuring the winged horse pegasus. A £500 with a diameter of 100mm and weight of one kilogram, featuring the stylised words 'XXX OLYMPIAD'.

Gold olympic themed coins coins consisted of 6x £25 coins (2 each for 'faster', 'higher' and 'stronger'), 3x £100 coins (one each for 'faster', 'higher' and 'stronger') and a crude looking one kilogram gold coin with a face value of £1000.

93

COMMEMORATIVE TYPE 24
Standard portrait of QEII
Design by: Ian Rank-Broadley
**Royal Wedding of William &
Catherine**
Design by: Mark Richards

		UNC	BU	Proof
2011		£7.00	£9.00	
	Specimen in folder		£20.00	
50,000 / 3000	.925 sterling silver proof / or gold plated coin			£40.00
3000 max	.925 sterling silver piedfort proof			£80.00
3000 max	.917 gold proof			£1200.00
200 max	Platinum piedfort proof			£4000.00

COMMEMORATIVE TYPE 25
Standard portrait of QEII
Design by: Ian Rank-Broadley
Countdown '1'
Design by: Claire Aldridge

		UNC	BU	Proof
2011		£6.00	£7.00	£10.00
	Specimen in folder		£10.00	
30,000 max	.925 sterling silver proof			£40.00
4000 max	.925 sterling silver piedfort proof			£80.00
3000 max	.917 gold proof			£1200.00

COMMEMORATIVE TYPE 26
Standard portrait of QEII
Design by: Ian Rank-Broadley
Prince Philip 90th Birthday
Design by: Mark Richards

		UNC	BU	Proof
2011		£5.50	£7.00	£10.00
	Specimen in folder		£10.00	
20,000 max	.925 sterling silver proof			£40.00
4000 max	.925 sterling silver piedfort proof			£80.00
1200 max	.917 gold proof			£1200.00
90 max	Platinum piedfort proof			£4000.00

COMMEMORATIVE TYPE 27
Standard portrait of QEII
Design by: Ian Rank-Broadley
Countdown '0'
Design by: Claire Aldridge

		UNC	BU	Proof
2012		£5.50	£7.00	£10.00
	Specimen in folder/card		£10.00	
30,000 max	.925 sterling silver proof			£40.00
4000 max	.925 sterling silver piedfort proof			£80.00
3000 max	.917 gold proof			£1200.00

COMMEMORATIVE TYPE 28
Standard portrait of QEII
Design by: Ian Rank-Broadley
London 2012 Olympics
Commemorative
Design by: Siaman Miah
Obverse: Type as no. 24

		UNC	BU	Proof
2012		£7.00	£9.00	
	Specimen in folder		£10.00	
100,000 max	.925 sterling silver proof			£30.00
7,000 max	.925 sterling silver piedfort proof			£100.00
12,500 max	.925 sterling silver, gold plating*			£
5000 max	.917 gold proof			£2500.00

COMMEMORATIVE TYPE 29
Standard portrait of QEII
Design by: Ian Rank-Broadley
London 2012 Paralympics
Commemorative
Design by: Pippa Sanderson
Obverse: Type as no. 24

		UNC	BU	Proof
2012		£5.50	£7.00	
	Specimen in folder		£10.00	
10,000/3000	.925 sterling silver proof / or gold plated version			£40.00
2012 max	.925 sterling silver piedfort proof			£100.00
5000 max	.917 gold proof			£2500.00

COMMEMORATIVE TYPE 30
Special portrait of QEII
Design by: Ian Rank-Broadley
Queen's Diamond Jubilee
Design by: Ian Rank-Broadley

		UNC	BU	Proof
2012		£5.50	£7.00	£10.00
	Specimen in folder		£10.00	
75,000 max	.925 sterling silver proof			£40.00
3,250 max	.925 sterling silver piedfort proof			£100.00
12,500 max	.925 sterling silver, gold plated*			£
3850 max	.917 gold proof			£2000.00
250 max	Platinum piedfort proof			£5000.00

To mark the Jubilee there was also a £10 coin (as silver or gold proof) with a diameter of 65mm - these have the same obverse as above and feature the queen enthroned and facing on the reverse. Prices new were about £450 for the silver version and £9,500 for the gold coin. One kilogram silver (£500) and one kilogram gold (£1000) coins were also made to mark the Queens jubilee. Both use the same obverse as above and show the full Royal Arms on the reverse.

COMMEMORATIVE TYPE 31
Standard portrait of QEII
Design by: Ian Rank-Broadley
Anniversary of Coronation
Design by: Emma Noble
Obverse: Type as no. 24

		UNC	BU	Proof
2013		£5.50	£7.00	£10.00
	Specimen in folder		£10.00	
	.925 sterling silver proof			£40.00
	.925 sterling silver piedfort proof			£100.00
	.925 sterling silver, gold plated*			£
	.917 gold proof			£1900.00
	Platinum Piedfort proof, price new			£6400.00

*Previously, the gold plating of silver coins was exclusively the reserve of dubious eBay sellers or private makers of coins in order to somehow justify the extortionate asking prices. It's not particularly hard to do, and I fail to see how a micro-thin layer of gold can add any value to a silver coin. I was shocked when I discovered that the Royal Mint had also taken the decision to make and sell gold plated silver coins.

97

COMMEMORATIVE TYPE 32
Standard portrait of QEII
Design by: Ian Rank-Broadley
Christening of Prince George
Design by: John Bergdahl

		UNC	BU	Proof
2013		£8.00	£10.00	
	Specimen in folder		£13.00	
75,000	.925 sterling silver proof			£30.00
	.925 sterling silver piedfort proof			£80.00
	.917 gold proof			£2000.00
St. George Rev	Initially a St.George proof version was issued*			£80.00

*Shortly after the birth of Prince George, a silver proof only £5 Crown was released with the Pistrucci St. George Reverse. This was the first coin that the Royal Mint suddenly refused to sell to other businesses, offering it exclusively to their private customers for £80.

Note that for both the 2013 coronation (no. 31) and Prince George (no.32) one kilo versions with a face value of £500 were struck in silver. These are both available new for £2600. A gold kilo version of no. 32 is currently available for £50,000!

COMMEMORATIVE TYPE 33
Standard portrait of QEII
Design by: Ian Rank-Broadley
300th Anniversary of the Death of Queen Anne
Design by: Mark Richards
Obverse: Type as no. 24

		UNC	BU	Proof
2014		£7.00	£9.00	
	Specimen in folder, new price		£13.00	
3100 max	.925 sterling silver proof			TBC
1665 max	.925 sterling silver, gold plated			TBC
2014 max	.925 sterling silver piedfort proof			TBC
300 max	.917 gold proof			TBC

The New £20 Coin

A new £20 silver coin was issued in 2013. It features the Rank-Broadly portrait of the Queen on the obverse, the Pistrucci St. George on the reverse and is about the size of the current £2 coin. It is available from the Royal Mint for £20.00 plus postage. The value of the silver content is about £7.00 which is not unusual as the face value of circulating coins has been less than the material value contained within for centuries. What confuses me though, is the legal tender status of the coin. The Royal Mint web site itself made no mention of a £20 coin being legal tender early in January 2014. By the end of January it has now been added to their list of legal tender coins (coins with £10 and £25 face value are currently still not shown). I'm no legal expert, but as far as I can tell the 'Coinage Act 1971' has not been amended since 2011 (a fairly minor change) and it makes no mention of a £20 being legal tender. Perhaps it will be amended.

My advice would be that people should by all means purchase the £20 coin as a medallic issue, but nothing more until its status as legal tender has been confirmed. There are certainly much better ways to invest in silver than spending £20 on £7 of silver! The coins are apparently accepted at the face value of £20 by certain banks, but who knows if this will be a permanent arrangement. Imagine this scenario: The value of silver falls in X years to half what it is now. The £20 coin now contains £3.50 of silver. Potentially lots of people may want to exchange their £20 coins at face value, and surely if the Banks have to pay £20 each for a flurry of coins worth substantially less than that, someone somewhere is going to lose out. And who is most likely to lose out; the banks, the Royal Mint or the man on the street?

United Kingdom Banknotes

The UK currently has four denominations of legal tender banknotes in circulation; the £5, £10, £20 and £50 notes. Some banks in Scotland and in Northern Ireland also issue Sterling banknotes in the same denomination as the Bank of England types (plus the Royal Bank of Scotland continues to issue smaller numbers of £1 notes). These notes are not officially legal tender but they are of course readily accepted within the countries in which they circulate. All of the Scottish and Northern Irish banknotes have to be backed up by Bank of England money; in other words, a bank issuing notes in Scotland or Northern Ireland has to theoretically hold in its vaults the same amount of Bank of England money. Usually this Bank of England money is held in the form of special high-value banknotes that are exchanged just between banks. The circulating Scottish and Northern Ireland banknotes are not covered in this book (perhaps in a future edition).

The four current circulating Bank of England notes are: £5 - Mainly green with Elizabeth Fry on the reverse. £10 - Mainly orange with Charles Darwin on the reverse. £20 - Mainly purple with Adam Smith on the reverse. £50 - Mainly red with Matthew Boulton and James Watt on the reverse.

The 'promise to pay the bearer' on each Bank of England banknote never expires, even when the notes of that type have long since been removed from circulation. As a result, every single Bank of England note can always be redeemed for its face value at the Bank of England, and usually at any UK bank. Shopkeepers and other merchants are not obliged to accept older Bank of England notes. Before redeeming older Bank of England notes it's obviously a good idea to check that they don't have a collectable worth first. This can be done using the Rotographic publication "Collectors' Banknotes" which is published regularly and includes valuations for all Bank of England and HM Treasury issued banknotes.

Banknote condition

Just as with coins, condition plays a very important role where the values of banknotes are concerned. Most collectors will attempt to collect the banknotes in the best condition they can afford. With modern banknotes this will nearly always be uncirculated (mint condition) examples, as such examples of modern banknotes are usually obtainable. With this in mind, most well-used, tatty, creased and dirty banknotes that have exchanged hands many times are only likely to be worth their face value. EF is an abbreviation for Extremely Fine and means that a note is in very good condition, but just a little way from being classed as UNCirculated. VF means Very Fine and is quite a common grade for modern notes that have seen limited average use.

Serial numbers

Collectors like interesting serial numbers too. If you ever get given a note with a low serial number, where at least the first 3 digits of the 6 digit number are zeros, keep hold of it. A note with the serial number AH43 000954 will be slightly more interesting than AH43 874563, for example. The note AH43 000001 would of course be more interesting still. AA01 000045 would be even more desirable! Collectors also like interesting patterns in numbers, like AH43 434343, AH22 222222 or AH12 345678. You won't get offered huge amounts of money for notes with interesting serial numbers, but you might persuade someone to give you slightly more than face value, assuming the note is in good condition.

Banknote images are © Bank of England.

Signed by <u>Merlyn Lowther</u>, the chief cashier of the Bank of England from 1999 to 2003.

DETAILS	EF	UNC

Letter, Letter, Number, Number, followed by 6 digits

DETAILS	EF	UNC
Number AA01 000000 Special Specimen note		£800.00
HA** followed by 6 digits (special first run)	£6.00	£14.00
HC01 followed by 6 digits (first prefix)	£25.00	£75.00
CL**, DL** or EL** then 6 digits (special column sort prefix)	£10.00	£20.00
XA** to XK** followed by 6 digits (varnish trial prefix)	£200.00	
LL** followed by 6 digits (replacement notes)	£10.00	£20.00
ER50 followed by 6 digits (special presentation pack issue)*		£25
HM02 followed by 6 digits (special presentation pack issue)*		£25
HM03 followed by 6 digits (special presentation pack issue)*		£25
QC03 followed by 6 digits (special presentation pack issue)*		£25
QC50 followed by 6 digits (special presentation pack issue)*		£25
JB** followed by 6 digits (last Lowther prefix)		£10.00

The first Elizabeth Fry £5 notes were withdrawn as the serial numbers were not properly varnished and could be partially rubbed off. Initially they were sought after and the extra demand meant they were worth slightly more. The affected notes were taken in, treated and then re released into circulation. None of the original issue now commands a premium.

* These notes were only issued as part of special sets.

Signed by <u>Andrew Bailey</u>, the chief cashier of the Bank of England from 2004 to 2011.

Letter, Letter, Number, Number, followed by 6 digits

DETAILS	EF	UNC
JB** followed by 6 digits (first prefix run)		£10.00
EL02 followed by 6 digits (special column sort prefix)	£10.00	£25.00
EL** followed by 6 digits (special column sort prefix)	£6.00	£12.00
LL** followed by 6 digits (replacement notes)	£10.00	£20.00
LE** followed by 6 digits (last Bailey prefix)		£10.00

Signed by <u>Chris Salmon</u>, the chief cashier of the Bank of England from 2011 to date.

Letter, Letter, Number, Number, followed by 6 digits

DETAILS	EF	UNC
LE** followed by 6 digits (first Salmon prefix)		£8.00

Signed by <u>Merlyn Lowther</u>, the chief cashier of the Bank of England from 1999 to 2003.

DETAILS	VF	EF	UNC
Letter, Letter, Number, Number, followed by 6 digits			
Number AA01 000000 Special Specimen note			£800.00
AA01 followed by 6 digits (first prefix)		£20.00	£50.00
AA01 followed by 6 digits (first prefix, worded 'and company')*¹		£30.00	£50.00
AD** followed by 6 digits (worded 'and company')*¹		£60.00	£120.00
AH80 followed by 6 digits (last prefix of first type) £50.00		£150.00	£300.00
AJ01 followed by 6 digits (first production run)		£50.00	£100.00
EL** followed by 6 digits (special column sort prefix)			£20.00
LL** followed by 6 digits (replacement notes)		£75.00	£150.00
LL** followed by 6 digits (replacement notes 'and company')*		£40.00	£90.00
CC80 followed by 6 digits (highest prefix known*²) £20.00		£75.00	£150.00
MH**, MJ**, MK**, MM** (experimental notes) £100.00		£150.00	
ER50 followed by 6 digits (special presentation pack issue)*			£30.00
QC50 followed by 6 digits (special presentation pack issue)*			£30.00
QV10 followed by 6 digits (special presentation pack issue)*			£30.00
VR10 followed by 6 digits (special presentation pack issue)*			£30.00

* These notes were only issued as part of special sets.

*¹ These notes have the wording 'The Governor and Company of the Bank of England' in the band of text above the central oval where the Queen's watermark appears. A variety exists with the wording 'The Governor <u>and the</u> Company of the Bank of England'. Both types were made in high numbers.

*[2] The CC** prefix overlaps with the CC** Bailey notes below. Until recently it was thought that CC40 was the last Lowther prefix. This is not that case as prefixes up to CC80 have been noted on newly issued Lowther notes.

Signed by <u>Andrew Bailey</u>, the chief cashier of the Bank of England from 2004 to 2011.

DETAILS	EF	UNC
Letter, Letter, Number, Number, followed by 6 digits		
CC41 followed by 6 digits (lowest known prefix)	£60.00	£120.00
EL** followed by 6 digits (special column sort prefix)	£15.00	£25.00
EL80 followed by 6 digits (last column sort EL prefix)	£50.00	£100.00
HL01 followed by 6 digits (first column sort HL prefix)	£50.00	£100.00
HL** followed by 6 digits (special column sort prefix)	£20.00	£50.00
LL** followed by 6 digits (replacement notes)	£15.00	£35.00
LA** followed by 6 digits (last Lowther prefix)	£15.00	£35.00

Signed by <u>Chris Salmon</u>, the chief cashier of the Bank of England from 2011 to date.

Letter, Letter, Number, Number, followed by 6 digits

Prefix JH** followed by 6 digits (first Salmon prefix)   £14.00

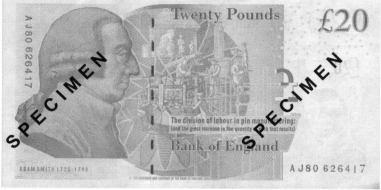

Signed by <u>Andrew Bailey</u>, the chief cashier of the Bank of England from 2004 to 2011.

DETAILS	EF	UNC
Letter, Letter, Number, Number, followed by 6 digits		
AA01 followed by 6 digits (first Bailey prefix)	£25.00	£50.00
AL** followed by 6 digits (special column sort prefix)	£25.00	£40.00
LL** followed by 6 digits (replacement notes)	£30.00	£50.00
HD36 followed by 6 digits (last Bailey prefix)		£35.00

Signed by <u>Chris Salmon</u> the chief cashier of the Bank of England from 2011 to date.

Letter, Letter, Number, Number, followed by 6 digits

	EF	UNC
HA** followed by 6 digits (first Salmon prefix)		£28.00

The Sir John Houblon note (shown above, and covered on the next page) is to be withdrawn from circulation on the 30th April 2014.

Banknote images are © Bank of England.

COLLECTORS' COINS - DECIMAL ISSUES OF THE UK

Signed by <u>G E A Kentfield</u>, the chief cashier of the Bank of England from 1991 to 1998.

The £50 is the only Kentfield note left in circulation. This is because the design has not been changed since these were issued in 1994 (it is due to be withdrawn in 2014, see previous page).

DETAILS	EF	UNC
Letter, Number, Number, followed by 6 digits		
A01 followed by 6 digits (first prefix)	£80.00	£150.00
H98 followed by 6 digits (last prefix)		£150.00
H99 followed by 6 digits (special print run for sets)		£150.00
L** followed by 6 digits (special column sort prefix)	£75.00	£130.00
A99 folowed by 6 digits (experimental prefix)	£100.00	£200.00
M99 followed by 6 digits (experimental prefix)	£200.00	£300.00
Letter, Letter, Number, Number, followed by 6 digits		
LL** followed by 6 digits (replacement note prefix)	£100.00	£220.00
Prefixes EP50, PW50, YR19 (special presentation pack issue)		£120.00

Signed by <u>Merlyn Lowther</u>, the chief cashier of the Bank of England from 1999 to 2003.

Letter, Number, Number, followed by 6 digits

	EF	UNC
J01 followed by 6 digits (first prefix)	£80.00	£150.00
K** or L** followed by 6 digits (special column sort prefix)	£90.00	£180.00
M35 followed by 6 digits (last prefix)	£80.00	£180.00

Signed by <u>Andrew Bailey</u>, the chief cashier of the Bank of England from 2004 to 2011.

Letter, Number, Number, followed by 6 digits

	EF	UNC
M01 followed by 6 digits (first prefix)	£70.00	£150.00
L** followed by 6 digits (special column sort prefix)	£70.00	£150.00

Signed by <u>Chris Salmon</u>, the chief cashier of the Bank of England from 2011 to date.

DETAILS

UNC

Letter, Number, Number, followed by 6 digits

AA** followed by 6 digits (first prefix)

£80.00

Banknote images are © Bank of England.

From 1971 to 1982, The Royal Mint issued proof coin sets sealed in plastic, enclosed in lightweight card envelopes. Generally the sets on this page sell for between £6.00 and £15.00.

Year	Pieces	Coins	Notes
1971	6	½p, 1p, 2p, 5p, 10p, 50p	
1972	7	½p, 1p, 2p, 5p, 10p, 25p, 50p	Silver Wedding crown
1973	6	½p, 1p, 2p, 5p, 10p, 50p	
1974	6	½p, 1p, 2p, 5p, 10p, 50p	
1975	6	½p, 1p, 2p, 5p, 10p, 50p	
1976	6	½p, 1p, 2p, 5p, 10p, 50p	
1977	7	½p, 1p, 2p, 5p, 10p, 25p, 50p	Silver Jubilee crown
1978	6	½p, 1p, 2p, 5p, 10p, 50p	
1979	6	½p, 1p, 2p, 5p, 10p, 50p	
1980	6	½p, 1p, 2p, 5p, 10p, 50p	
1981	6	½p, 1p, 2p, 5p, 10p, 50p	
1982	7	½p, 1p, 2p, 5p, 10p, 20p, 50p	new 20p added

In 1983, the packaging was changed to a blue leatherette bookshelf type case.

Year	Pieces	Coins	Notes
1983	8	½p, 1p, 2p, 5p, 10p, 20p, 50p, £1	new £1 added
1984	8	½p, 1p, 2p, 5p, 10p, 20p, 50p, £1	

From 1985 onward, two types of packaging were offered: The "standard" blue leatherette case, and the "deluxe" red leather case. 1985 to 1999 sets are worth between £10.00 up to around £25.00.

Year	Pieces	Coins	Notes
1985	7	1p, 2p, 5p, 10p, 20p, 50p, £1	½p removed
1986	8	1p, 2p, 5p, 10p, 20p, 50p, £1, £2	Commonwealth Games
1987	7	1p, 2p, 5p, 10p, 20p, 50p, £1	
1988	7	1p, 2p, 5p, 10p, 20p, 50p, £1	
1989	9	1p, 2p, 5p, 10p, 20p, 50p, £1, £2, £2	Bill of Rights/Claim of Right
1990	8	1p, 2p, 5p, 5p, 10p, 20p, 50p, £1	Both 5p sizes
1991	7	1p, 2p, 5p, 10p, 20p, 50p, £1	
1992	9	1p, 2p, 5p, 10p, 10p, 20p, 50p, 50p, £1	Both 10p sizes; EEC 50p
1993	8	1p, 2p, 5p, 10p, 20p, 50p, £1, £5	Coronation Anniversary
1994	8	1p, 2p, 5p, 10p, 20p, 50p, £1, £2	Bank of England
1995	8	1p, 2p, 5p, 10p, 20p, 50p, £1, £2	Dove of Peace
1996	9	1p, 2p, 5p, 10p, 20p, 50p, £1, £2, £5	Football; 70th Birthday
1997	10	1p, 2p, 5p, 10p, 20p, 50p, 50p, £1, £2, £5	Both 50p's; Royal Wedding
1998	10	1p, 2p, 5p, 10p, 20p, 50p, 50p, £1, £2, £5	EU; Prince Charles
1999	9	1p, 2p, 5p, 10p, 20p, 50p, £1, £2, £5	Rugby, Princess Diana

From 2000 on, it is accepted that all sets will contain the standard 8 pieces: 1p, 2p, 5p, 10p, 20p, 50p, £1, and £2. The Royal Mint, also produce deluxe proof sets and executive proof sets, which contain the same coins but have better packaging. The deluxe and executive sets are often sold for a few pounds more than the standard sets. Sets dated 2000 to 2004 are worth around £30.00. Later sets are worth slightly more and usually the most recent are still available new for the Royal Mint retail price, which is currently around £60 - £100.

Recently 'Premium' sets have been introduced which include a medallion! And in 2013 the RM made the proof sets available in 'definitive' form, which include just the standard 1p to £2, a 'commemorative' set which is just the commemorative 50p, £1 and £2 coins and also a complete set made up of all the coins. I'm starting to lose track, and I honestly don't think the packaging will play much of a roll in the future - the coins are what they are, regardless of the current sales-packaging-strategy!

Year	Pieces	Commemorative issues
2000	10	50p Public Libraries, £5 Millennium
2001	10	£2 Marconi, £5 Victorian Era
2002	9	£5 Coronation Jubilee
2003	11	50p Women's Suffrage, £2 DNA, £5 Golden Jubilee
2004	10	50p Roger Bannister, £2 Trevithick's Steam Locomotive
2005	12	50p Johnson's Dictionary, £2 Guy Fawkes, £5 Nelson, £5 Trafalgar
2006	13	Both VC 50p's, Both Brunel £2's, £5 Queen's 80th Birthday
2007	12	50p Scouting, Union £2 and Slave Trade £2, Diamond Wedding £5
2008	11	Olypic Centenary £2, Charles £5, Elizabeth I £5
2009	12	Kew 50p, Darwin £2, Burns £2, Henry VIII £5
2010	13	Girl Guides 50p, London £1, Belfast £1, Nursing £2, Restoration £5
2011	14	WWF 50p, Edinburgh £1, Cardiff £1, Bible £2, Mary Rose £2, Philip £5
2012	10	Dickens £2, Accession £5
2013	15	Ironside 50p, Floral £1 x2, Underground £2 x2, Guinea £2, Coronation £5
2014	14	Games 50p, Floral £1 x2, WWI £2, Trinity £2, Queen Anne £5

In 1982, the Royal Mint introduced BU sets, which contain most of the coins contained in the Proof sets (crowns normally not included). These sets do not have the proof quality striking, and are packaged in a folder style, but they do provide history background text on the coins.

Year	Pieces	Coins	Notes
1982	7	½p, 1p, 2p, 5p, 10p, 20p, 50p	
1983	8	½p, 1p, 2p, 5p, 10p, 20p, 50p, £1	new £1 added
1984	8	½p, 1p, 2p, 5p, 10p, 20p, 50p, £1	
1985	7	1p, 2p, 5p, 10p, 20p, 50p, £1	½p removed
1986	8	1p, 2p, 5p, 10p, 20p, 50p, £1, £2	Commonwealth Games
1987	7	1p, 2p, 5p, 10p, 20p, 50p, £1	
1988	7	1p, 2p, 5p, 10p, 20p, 50p, £1	
1989	7	1p, 2p, 5p, 10p, 20p, 50p, £1	
1990	8	1p, 2p, 5p, 5p, 10p, 20p, 50p, £1	lg & sm 5p
1991	7	1p, 2p, 5p, 10p, 20p, 50p, £1	
1992	9	1p, 2p, 5p, 10p, 10p, 20p, 50p, 50p, £1	lg & sm 10p; EEC
1993	8	1p, 2p, 5p, 10p, 20p, 50p, £1, £5	Coronation Anniversary
1994	8	1p, 2p, 5p, 10p, 20p, 50p, £1, £2	Bank of England
1995	8	1p, 2p, 5p, 10p, 20p, 50p, £1, £2	Dove of Peace
1996	8	1p, 2p, 5p, 10p, 20p, 50p, £1, £2	Football
1997	9	1p, 2p, 5p, 10p, 20p, 50p, 50p, £1, £2	lg & sm 50p
1998	9	1p, 2p, 5p, 10p, 20p, 50p, 50p, £1, £2	EU
1999	8	1p, 2p, 5p, 10p, 20p, 50p, £1, £2	Rugby
2000	9	1p, 2p, 5p, 10p, 20p, 50p, 50p, £1, £2	Public Libraries
2001	9	1p, 2p, 5p, 10p, 20p, 50p, £1, £2, £2	Marconi
2002	8	1p, 2p, 5p, 10p, 20p, 50p, £1, £2	
2003	10	1p, 2p, 5p, 10p, 20p, 50p, 50p, £1, £2, £2	Women's Suffrage, DNA
2004	10	1p, 2p, 5p, 10p, 20p, 50p, 50p, £1, £2, £2	Bannister, Trevithick
2005	10	1p, 2p, 5p, 10p, 20p, 50p, 50p, £1, £2, £2	Dictionary, Guy Fawkes
2006	10	1p, 2p, 5p, 10p, 20p, 50p, 50p, £1, £2, £2	Victoria Cross, Brunel
2007	9	1p, 2p, 5p, 10p, 20p., 50p, £1, £2, £2	Slave trade, Act of Union
2008	9	1p, 2p, 5p, 10p, 20p, 50p, £1, £2, £2	Old designs. Olympic £2.
2009	11	1p, 2p, 5p, 10p, 20p, 50p, 50p, £1, £2, £2, £2	Kew, Burns, Darwin.
2010	8	1p, 2p, 5p, 10,p 20p, 50p, £1, £2	
2011	13	1p, 2p, 5p, 10p, 20p, 50p, 50p, £1 x3, £2 x3	
2012	10	1p, 2p, 5p, 10p, 20p, 50p, £1, £2, £2, £5	
2013	15	1p, 2p, 5p, 10p, 20p, 50p x2, £1 x3, £2 x4, £5	
2014	14	1p, 2p, 5p, 10p, 20p, 50p x2, £1 x3, £2 x3, £5	

The above sets tend to sell from between 2x to 3x the face value of the coins included. Sets in mint condition with absolutely no toning on any of the coins will attract a premium. At the time of writing the 2009 set is affected by the Kew Gardens 50p hype. See 50p Commemorative Type 13 for further details. 106,332 of the 2009 set were sold.

Year	Pieces	Coins
1983	7	½p, 1p, 2p, 5p, 10p, 20p, 50p Specially packaged set for the H J Heinz Company.
1983	8	½p, 1p, 2p, 5p, 10p, 20p, 50p, £1 Specially packaged set for the Martini & Rossi Company.
1988	7	1p, 2p, 5p, 10p, 20p, 50p, £1 Special package celebrating Australia's Bicentennial.
1996	14 (7+7)	1p, 2p, 5p, 10p, 20p, 50p, £1; pre-decimal 1/2d, 1d, 3d, 6d, 1/, 2/, 2/6d Special package commemorating 25 years of decimalisation.
2000	9	1p,2p,5p,10p,20p,50p,£1,£2, £5 (Millennium) In special "Time Capsule" packaging.
2004	3	50p (Roger Bannister), £1 (Forth bridge), £2 (Trevithick's Locomotive) "Celebrating Human Achievement"
2005	3	50p (Johnson's dictionary), £1 (Menai bridge), £2 (Guy Fawkes) new packaging of commemorative issues

The sets above were specially marketed for commemorative or promotional purposes. Other sets exist and will be included in a future edition.

INFO

1998 saw the introduction of yet another Royal Mint packaging, the "Baby Pack". These sets contain the same coins as the normal BU sets, but the packaging is oriented as gifts for newborn children, Continuing on this course, in 1999, the "Wedding Pack" was introduced.

The following are sterling (.925) silver proof sets, designed for various occasions, including the introduction of the coins themselves. These are normally found in hard acrylic capsules, enclosed in a clam-shell case, and with a certificate from the Royal Mint. Loose pieces, without the case and/or certificate, sell at a deep discount, up to 40% less. Some issues later than 1998 are included in the main section.

Five Pence

1990	35,000	large & small sized pair	£25.00

Ten Pence

1992	35,000	large & small sized pair	£25.00

Fifty Pence

1997	10,304	large & small sized pair	£25.00
1998	22,078	NHS issue and EU issue pair	£55.00
1998		pair, EU silver proof & EU silver Piedfort	£70.00

One Pound

1983 - 88	1,000	set of 6 regional designs, Arms, Shield	£75.00
1984 - 87	50,000	set of 4 regional designs	£90.00
1994 - 97	25,000	set of 4 regional designs	£100.00
1999 - 2002	25,000	set of 4 regional designs	£100.00

Two Pounds

1989	25,000	Bill of Rights & Claim of Rights pair	£60.00
1997	40,000	new bi-metallic circulation issue	£20.00
1998	25,000	new portrait on the circulation issue	£20.00
1997/98		bi-metallic Maklouf & Rank-Broadley pair	£35.00

1981	5,000	set, all issues, 1/2p-50p in base metals, sterling 25p commemorative, 22k gold Sovereign & £5	£700.00
1981		pair, sterling 25p commemorative, 22k gold Sovereign	£70.00
1992	1,000	set, both lg and sm 10p, 50p EEC, and £1	£75.00
1993	1,000	set, 50p EEC, £1, and £5 Coronation commem.	£75.00
1994	2,000	set, 50p D-Day, £1, and £2 Bank of England	£70.00
1995	1,000	silver set, peace £2, UN £2 and £1 coin	£50.00
1996	1,000	silver set, £5, £2 and £1 coins	£50.00
1996		set, all issues, 1p-£1 (25th Anniversary of Decimalisation)	£70.00
	500	pair, 1996 70th Birthday crown & 1997 Royal Wedding Jubilee crown	£60.00
1997		set, 50p, £1, £2, £5 Wedding Jubilee, £2 Britannia	£120.00
1999		set, £5 Millennium, £2 Britannia	£40.00
1999		set, £2 Britannia, £10 stamp	
2000	13,180	set, 1p-£5 Millennium, plus Maundy set (13 pieces)	£200.00
2000		£5 Millennium, plus YR2000 serial numbered £20 note	
		pair, 2002 Silver Jubilee crown & 2003 Coronation Jubilee crown	£60.00
2004		pair, 2004 Entente Cordiale crown & French €1 1/2 commem.	£75.00
2004	750	set, 50p Bannister, £1 Forth Bridge, £2 Trevithick, £5 Entente Cordiale £2 Britannia.	£75.00
asst'd		1999, 2001, 2002, 2003 £2 Britannia uncirculated.	£45.00

The following set was struck in .917 (22K) gold.

2002	2,002	set, 1p-£5 Golden Jubilee, plus Maundy set (13 pieces)	£750.00

ALERT

It seems that official Royal Mint cases were obtainable, and some of these sets were assembled on the secondary market, with the individual coins and accompanying certificates. Original RM-issued sets usually contain a single certificate, listing each coin in the set.

Piedforts are pieces that are double the thickness and weight of normal pieces, and are almost always struck in sterling (.925) silver. These are normally found in hard acrylic capsules, enclosed in a clam-shell case, and with a certificate from the Royal Mint. Loose pieces, without the case and/or certificate sell at a deep discount, up to 40% less.

Five Pence
1990	20,000	.925 sterling silver, small size Piedfort	£20.00

Ten Pence
1992	.925 sterling silver, small size Piedfort	£30.00

Twenty Pence
1982	.925 sterling silver, Piedfort	£30.00

Fifty Pence
1997	7,192	.925 sterling silver, small size Piedfort	£50.00
1998		EEC & NHS pair, Piedfort	£30.00

One Pound
1983 - 88	500	set of 6 regional designs, Arms, Shield, Piedfort	£250.00
1984 - 87	10,000	.925 sterling silver, proof set of 4 Piedfort	£175.00
1994 - 97		.925 sterling silver, proof set of 4 Piedfort	£190.00
1999-2002	10,000	.925 sterling silver, proof set of 4 Piedfort	£225.00
2004-2007	1,400	.925 sterling silver, proof set of 4 Piedfort	£200.00

Two Pounds
1989	10,000	Bill of Rights & Claim of Rights pair, Piedfort	£30.00
1997	10,000	.925 sterling silver, Piedfort	£55.00
1998	10,000	.925 sterling silver, Piedfort £55	
1997/98	.10,000	925 sterling silver, Piedfort (pair)	£125.00
1999	10,000	.925 sterling silver, proof Piedfort HOLOGRAM	£100.00

Five Pounds
2005	Nelson & Trafalgar pair, Piedfort	£125.00

Sets

2003		set, 50p WPSU, £1 Royal Arms, £2 DNA Piedfort	£60.00
2004	7500	set, 50p Bannister, £1 Forth Bridge, £2 Trevithick Piedfort	£150.00
2005		set, 50p Johnson's Dictionary, £1 Menai Bridge, £2 GunPowder Plot, £2 World War II Piedfort	£150.00
2007		£5, both £2 coins, £1 and 50p Piedfort	£250.00
2008		2x £5 coins, £2 and £1 Piedfort	£250.00
2008		The 7 new Dent design coins as silver Piedforts	£350.00
2009		Piedfort gold proof set of 16x difference 50 pences	£ EXPENSIVE
2010		£5, £2, both £1 coins and the 50p	£300.00
2010 / 2011		Capital cities 4x £1 set	£300.00
2013		4x £5 coins, each with different Queen portrait	£683.00 new price
2013		The 5 Commemorative coins + the 2 £1 coins	£560.00 new price
2013		Pair of London Underground £2 coins	£200.00 new price
2014		The 4 Commemorative coins + the 2 £1 coins	£575.00 new price

Special Collector Issues (Patterns)

A trial bi-metallic piece was issued in 1994 (predecessor to the £2 bi-metallic). The obverse shows a cutty (ship), while the reverse carries the Maklouf portrait of QEII. The ring bears the legend "ROYAL MINT TRIAL PATTERN", and an edge legend of 'ANNO REGNIA XLVI, DECUS ET TUTAMEN". See the £2 section.

Pattern sets issued by the Royal Mint to preview the new issue of "Bridges" £1 coins. All of these coins carry the date of 2003, and rather than having a face value, they are labelled as "PATTERN".

2003	7,500	.925 sterling silver, 7,500 , proof set of 4	£100.00
	3,000	.917 gold proof set of 4	£1,200.00

A continuation of the above set, this set shows the "Beasts" series, which was a runner-up in the design competition for the new £1 coinage. All of these coins carry the date of 2004, and rather than having a face value, they are labelled as "PATTERN". Issued, as listed, in both sterling (.925) silver, and 22k (.917) gold.

2004	5,000	.925 sterling silver, proof set of 4	£95.00
	2,250	.917 gold proof set of 4	£975.00

Silver Britannia issues began in 1997 with proof-only coins. Commencing in 1998, the RM has followed a pattern of using the standard Standing Britannia for every other year (even years), while bringing out new unique designs for the odd years. I believe the whole point of these Britannia issues was the fact that they were struck in Britannia silver (.9584 fine) which made them a little special. From 2013 the proof versions are it seems, now struck in .999 silver. I don't understand the logic behind that change.

In 2014 the RM have introduced another bullion range of coins, in .999 silver and also a single coin in .9999 gold. They are, according to the blurb: 'Celebrating Chinese and British heritage with a dynamic design'. A horse, by Wuon-Gean Ho.

Bullion .958 Silver (UNC) £2 issues

1998	88,909	Standing Britannia	£23.00
1999	69,394	Britannia in Chariot	£23.00
2000	81,301	Standing Britannia	£23.00
2001	44,816	Una & the Lion	£23.00
2002	48,215	Standing Britannia	£23.00
2003	73,271	Helmeted Britannia facing left	£23.00
2004	100,000	Standing Britannia	£23.00
2005	100,000	Britannia seated	£23.00
2006		Standing Britannia	£23.00
2007		Britannia seated	£23.00
2008		Standing Britannia	£23.00
2009		Britannia standing in Chariot	£23.00
2010		Bust of Britannia in profile	£23.00
2011		Sitting Britannia	£23.00
2012		Standing Britannia	£23.00
2013		Standing Britannia	£23.00
2014		Standing Britannia	£25.00

.958 Silver (PROOF) issues

1997	£2	4,173	Britannia in Chariot	£50.00
	20p	8,686		£20.00
1998	£2	2,168	Standing Britannia	£90.00
	20p	2,724		£20.00
2001	£2	3,047	Britannia with Lion	£60.00
	20p	826		£20.00
2003	£2	1,833	Britannia wearing Roman Helmet	£60.00
	20p	1,003		£20.00
2004	£2	5,000	Standing Britannia	£60.00
2005	£2	2,500	Britannia seated	£60.00
2006	£2	2,500	Standing Britannia	£60.00
2007	£2		Britannia seated	£60.00
2007	20p			£25.00

.958 Silver (PROOF) issues

2008	20p		Standing Britannia	£60.00
	£2			£25.00
2009	£2		Britannia standing in Chariot	£70.00
2010	£2		Bust of Britannia in profile	£65.00
	20p			£25.00
2011	£2		Sitting Britannia	£60.00
	20p			£25.00
2012	£2		Standing Britannia	£50.00
	20p			£
2013	£2		Sitting Britiannia now .999	None available separately

Special (PROOF) sets

1997		11,832	Set of 4 (£2, £1, 50p, 20p)	£140.00
1998		3,044	Set of 4 (£2, £1, 50p, 20p)	£170.00
2001		4,596	Set of 4 (£2, £1, 50p, 20p)	£130.00
2003		3,623	Set of 4 (£2, £1, 50p, 20p)	£130.00
2005		5,000	Set of 4 (£2, £1, 50p, 20p)	£130.00
2006		–	Set of 5x different £2 with gold plated details	£210.00
2007		2,500	Set of 4 (£2, £1, 50p, 20p)	£130.00
2008			Set of 4 (£2, £1, 50p, 20p)	£170.00
2009			Set of 4 (£2, £1, 50p, 20p)	£150.00
2010			Set of 4 (£2, £1, 50p, 20p)	£150.00
2011			Set of 4 (£2, £1, 50p, 20p)	£180.00
2012			Set of 4 (£2, £1, 50p, 20p)	£250.00
2013	Now in .999 silver		Set of 5 (£2, £1, 50p, 20p, 10p)	£200.00 new price
			Pair of 20p and 10p	£37.50 new price

Platinum 2007 Coins were issued to mark the 20th Anniversary of the 'Britannia'

2007	£10		1/10 oz Platinum	£200.00
2007	£25		1/4 oz Platinum	£450.00
2007		250	Set of 4 Platinum coins	£3000.00

Lunar Bullion/Proof coins, issue prices (for a picture of this design, see the last page):

2014		One Ounce proof .999 Silver / Two Pounds	£82.50
2014		Five Ounce proof .999 Silver / Ten Pounds	£450.00
2014		Tenth Ounce .9999 Gold / Ten Pounds	£225.00

Gold Britannia issues began in 1987, as both bullion issues as well as proof issues. The values of the bullion issues are based on the value of the gold content, which fluctuates daily. The prices for these issues are given only as a guideline.

Bullion .917 Gold (UNC) Issues

£10	tenth ounce	Bullion Value + 30 to 50%
£25	quarter ounce	Bullion Value + 12 to 25%
£50	half ounce	Bullion Value + 8 to 20%
£100	one ounce	Bullion Value + 5 to 15%

The following are 4-piece sets, each coin encapsulated, and housed in a clamshell case,.

Special PROOF sets of 4 coins (for some dates, 3 or 5 coin sets were issued)

1987	10,000	Britannia standing	£1900.00
1988	3,505	Britannia standing	£1925.00
1989	2,268	Britannia standing	£2000.00
1990	527	Britannia standing	£1950.00
1991	509	Britannia standing	£1900.00
1992	500	Britannia standing	£1900.00
1993	462	Britannia standing	£1925.00
1994	435	Britannia standing	£1950.00
1995	500	Britannia standing	£2000.00
1996	483	Britannia standing	£2000.00
1997	892	Britannia standing	£2000.00
1998	750	Britannia standing	£2000.00
1999	750	Britannia standing	£2050.00
2000	750	Britannia standing	£2000.00
2001	1,000	Una & the Lion	£2000.00
2002	945	Britannia standing	£1700.00
2003	1,250	Britannia with Helmet	£1700.00
2004	973	Britannia standing	£1700.00
2005	1,439	Britannia seated	£1700.00
2006	1,163	Britannia standing	£1700.00
2007	1,250	Britannia seated	£1700.00
2008	1,250	Britannia standing	£1700.00
2009		Britannia standing in chariot	£1700.00
2010		Britannia bust in profile	£2200.00
2011		4 coin set	£2500.00
		3 coin set	£1300.00
2012		Britannia standing	£2200.00
2013		Now .9999 gold	£2900.00 new price
		3 coin set	£?
2014			

Britannia (PROOF) invividual cased coins

£100	1997	£1000.00
£100	Other dates	£850.00-£1000.00
£50	All dates	£450.00-£600.00
£25	All dates	£230.00-£350.00
£10	All dates	Around £100.00-£150.00

Gold Sovereign-based single coins are defined as non-commemorative Five Pounds, Two Pounds, Sovereigns and Half Sovereigns struck to normal or proof standards and sold singularly as gold bullion coins or as proof collectors' coins. The non-proof coins do not have boxes or certificates and are normally just traded as gold. Sovereigns and half sovereigns are 22 carat gold (.917 fine) and weigh 7.98g and 3.97g respectively.

Five Pounds

1984	Cased proof only	£1200.00
1984	Cased proof only with 'U' in circle next to date	£1100.00
1985	Cased proof only	£1200.00
1985	with 'U' in circle next to date	£1100.00
1986	with 'U' in circle next to date	£1100.00
1987	with 'U' in circle next to date	£1100.00
1988	with 'U' in circle next to date	£1100.00
1989	Sovereign Anniversary type	£1200.00
1989	Sovereign Anniversary type, cased proof	£1300.00
1990	with 'U' in circle next to date	£1150.00
1991	with 'U' in circle next to date	£1150.00
1992	with 'U' in circle next to date	£1150.00
1993	with 'U' in circle next to date	£1150.00
1994	with 'U' in circle next to date	£1150.00
1995	with 'U' in circle next to date	£1150.00
1996	with 'U' in circle next to date	£1150.00
1997	with 'U' in circle next to date	£1200.00
1998	New portrait	£1200.00
1999		£1200.00
2000		£1200.00
2000	with 'U' in circle next to date	£1200.00
2001		£1200.00
2002	Shield reverse	£1200.00
2003 to 2010		£1300.00
2011		£1600.00
2012		£1600.00
2013 & 2014		£2000.00

Two Pounds (double sovereign)

All are cased proofs. The £2 coin has not often been issued on its own.

1987		£300.00
1988		£300.00
1989	Sovereign Anniversary type	£350.00
1990		£300.00
1991		£300.00
1992		£300.00
1993		£300.00
1994	(see 1994 error commemorative type 4 £2 coin)	
1996		£300.00

Sovereigns, loose bullion type

Sovereigns of the 1970s and 1980s are generally traded at their bullion value. They contain 7.32 grammes of fine gold. Particularly perfect examples may be worth a slight premium. The dates struck were as follows:

1974, 1976, 1978, 1979, 1980, 1981 and 1982   Bullion Value

Modern bullion type sovereigns, from 2000 to date, tend to sell for a little more than bullion value as follows:

£180.00 to £230.00

Sovereigns, cased proof type

1979		£200.00
1980		£200.00
1981		£200.00
1982		£200.00
1983		£200.00
1984		£210.00
1985		£220.00
1986		£210.00
1987		£210.00
1988		£220.00
1989	500th Anniversary of the Sovereign	£600.00
1990		£240.00
1991		£240.00
1992		£250.00
1993		£250.00
1994		£250.00
1995		£250.00
1996		£250.00
1997		£250.00
1998		£250.00
1999		£250.00
2000		£260.00
2001		£260.00
2002		£260.00
2003		£260.00
2004		£260.00
2005 to 2012		£300.00
2013		£300.00
2014		

Half Sovereigns, loose bullion type

Until recently, the 1982 Half Sovereign was the only non-proof coin and continues to trade at approximately bullion value. In 2000 the Royal Mint started issuing non-proof half sovereigns and have done so each year since. The 2000 to 2007 half sovereigns tend to trade from about £100 to £120 (based on the bullion value at the time of writing). The shield reverse 2002 coin and the St. George 2005 coin are the most popular.

Half Sovereigns, cased proof type

1979		£100.00
1980		£100.00
1981		£100.00
1982		£100.00
1983		£100.00
1984		£100.00
1985		£100.00
1986		£100.00
1987		£100.00
1988		£100.00
1989	500th Anniversary of the Sovereign	£200.00
1990		£120.00
1991		£120.00
1992		£130.00
1993		£130.00
1994		£130.00
1995		£130.00
1996		£130.00
1997		£130.00
1998		£130.00
1999		£130.00
2000		£130.00
2001		£130.00
2002		£140.00
2003		£140.00
2004		£130.00
2005		£130.00
2006		£140.00
2007		£140.00
2008 to 2011		£150.00
2012		£150.00
2013		£150.00

Quarter Sovereigns

Introduced in 2009 as a completely made-up denomination - they seem to sell for £65 - £100 both bullion and proof issue.

1980	10,000	£5, £2, Sovereign (£1), 1/2 Sovereign	£1700.00
1981	–	Set containing 9 coins including silver Crown	£1000.00
1982	2,500	£5, £2, Sovereign (£1), 1/2 Sovereign	£1700.00
1983		£2, Sovereign (£1), 1/2 Sovereign	£900.00
1984	7,095	£5, Sovereign (£1), 1/2 Sovereign	£1350.00
1985	5,849	£5, £2, Sovereign (£1), 1/2 Sovereign	£1800.00
1986	12,000	£2 Commonwealth Games, Sovereign (£1), 1/2 Sovereign	£1000.00
1987	12,500	£2, Sovereign (£1), 1/2 Sovereign	£850.00
1988	12,500	£2, Sovereign (£1), 1/2 Sovereign	£950.00
1989	5,000	£5, £2, Sovereign (£1), 1/2 Sovereign (Anniversary reverse)	£3000.00
	7,936	£2, Sovereign (£1), 1/2 Sovereign (Anniversary reverse)	£2000.00
1990	1,721	£5, £2, Sovereign (£1), 1/2 Sovereign	£2000.00
	1,937	£2, Sovereign (£1), 1/2 Sovereign	£1000.00
1991	1,336	£5, £2, Sovereign (£1), 1/2 Sovereign	£2000.00
	1,152	£2, Sovereign (£1), 1/2 Sovereign	£1000.00
1992	1,165	£5, £2, Sovereign (£1), 1/2 Sovereign	£2000.00
	967	£2, Sovereign (£1), 1/2 Sovereign	£1000.00
1993	1,078	£5, £2, Sovereign (£1), 1/2 Sovereign (Pistrucci medallion)	£2200.00
	663	£2, Sovereign (£1), 1/2 Sovereign	£1200.00
1994	918	£5, £2 (Bank of England), Sovereign (£1), 1/2 Sovereign	£2000.00
	1,249	£2 (Bank of England), Sovereign (£1), 1/2 Sovereign	£1100.00
1995	718	£5, £2 (Dove of Peace), Sovereign (£1), 1/2 Sovereign	£2000.00
	1,112	£2 (Dove of Peace), Sovereign (£1), 1/2 Sovereign	£1200.00
1996	742	£5, £2, Sovereign (£1), 1/2 Sovereign	£2000.00
	868	£2, Sovereign (£1), 1/2 Sovereign	£1200.00
1997	860	£5, £2 (bi-metallic), Sovereign (£1), 1/2 Sovereign	£2000.00
	817	£2 (bi-metallic), Sovereign (£1), 1/2 Sovereign	£1200.00
1998	789	£5, £2, Sovereign (£1), 1/2 Sovereign	£2000.00
	560	£2, Sovereign (£1), 1/2 Sovereign	£1100.00
1999	991	£5, £2 (Rugby World Cup), Sovereign (£1), 1/2 Sovereign	£2000.00
	912	£2 (Rugby World Cup), Sovereign (£1), 1/2 Sovereign	£1300.00
2000	1,000	£5, £2, Sovereign (£1), 1/2 Sovereign	£2100.00
	1,250	£2, Sovereign (£1), 1/2 Sovereign	£1200.00

2001	1,000	£5, £2 (Marconi), Sovereign (£1), 1/2 Sovereign	£2100.00
	891	£2 (Marconi), Sovereign (£1), 1/2 Sovereign	£1200.00
2002	3,000	£5, £2, Sovereign (£1), 1/2 Sovereign (Shield reverse)	£2400.00
	3,947	£2, Sovereign (£1), 1/2 Sovereign.(Shield reverse)	£1400.00
2003	2,250	£5, £2, Sovereign (£1), 1/2 Sovereign	£2000.00
	1,717	£2 (DNA), Sovereign (£1), 1/2 Sovereign	£1100.00
2004	2,250	£5, £2, Sovereign (£1), 1/2 Sovereign	£2000.00
	2,500	£2, £1 (Forth Bridge), 1/2 Sovereign	£1100.00
2005	1,500	£5, £2, Sovereign (£1), 1/2 Sovereign	£2100.00
	2,500	£2, Sovereign (£1), 1/2 Sovereign	£1100.00
2006	1,750	£5, £2, Sovereign (£1), 1/2 Sovereign	£2000.00
	1,750	£2, Sovereign (£1), 1/2 Sovereign	£1200.00
2007		Sovereign, 1/2 Sovereign	£450.00
	700	£2, Sovereign, 1/2 Sovereign	£1200.00
2008		Sovereign, 1/2 Sovereign	£450.00
		£5, £2, Sovereign, 1/2 Sovereign	£2000.00
		£2, Sovereign, 1/2 Sovereign	£1100.00
2009		£5, £2, Sovereign, 1/2 Sovereign and new 1/4 Sovereign	£2400.00
		£2, Sovereign, 1/2 Sovereign and new 1/4 Sovereign	£1050.00
2010		£5, £2, Sovereign, 1/2 Sovereign, 1/4 Sovereign. Issue price	£2550.00
		Sovereign, 1/2 Sovereign, 1/4 Sovereign. Issue price	£550.00
		'Premium' set, 3 coins as above. Issue price	£1030.00

Values of later sets are similar. They are much more expensive when bought new.

Based on a tradition dating back to the 12th century, every year on Maundy Thursday (the day before Good Friday), the monarch distributes leather pouches of special coins to selected people in a Royal Ceremony. The number of recipients is equal to the age of the monarch, as is the value of the coins in each pouch.

All Maundy coinage issued under the reign of Queen Elizabeth II carries the same obverse portrait, that of the first bust of the Queen used on coins and designed by Mary Gillick.

Prices listed here are for complete sets in official Royal Mint cases, which became standard in in the 1960s. Commencing in 1989, the coins are individually encapsulated within the case.

1971	1,018	Tewkesbury Abbey	£120.00
1972	1,026	York Minster	£130.00
1973	1,004	Westminster Abbey	£120.00
1974	1,042	Salisbury Cathedral	£120.00
1975	1,050	Peterborough Cathedral	£120.00
1976	1,158	Hereford Cathedral	£120.00
1977	1,138	Westminster Abbey	£120.00
1978	1,178	Carlisle Cathedral	£120.00
1979	1,188	Winchester Cathedral	£120.00
1980	1,198	Worcester Cathedral	£120.00
1981	1,178	Westminster Abbey	£120.00
1982	1,218	St. David's Cathedral, Dyfed	£120.00
1983	1,228	Exeter Cathedral	£120.00
1984	1,238	Southwell Minster	£120.00
1985	1,248	Ripon Cathedral	£130.00
1986	1,378	Chichester Cathedral	£120.00
1987	1,390	Ely Cathedral	£120.00
1988	1,402	Lichfield Cathedral	£120.00
1989	1,353	Birmingham Cathedral	£120.00
1990	1,523	Newcastle Cathedral	£120.00
1991	1,384	Westminster Abbey	£120.00
1992	1,424	Chester Cathedral	£120.00
1993	1,440	Wells Cathedral	£120.00
1994	1,433	Truro Cathedral	£120.00

INFO

On "Decimalisation Day" in 1971, all Maundy money was re-valued to decimal pence (the old 1d pieces became worth 1p decimal). Since 1971, the coins have the face value of 1p, 2p, 3p, 4p although there is no significant change in design to note this transition.

1995	1,466	Coventry Cathedral	£120.00
1996	1,629	Norwich Cathedral	£120.00
1997	1,786	Bradford Cathedral	£130.00
1998	1,654	Portsmouth Cathedral	£120.00
1999	1,676	Bristol Cathedral	£120.00
2000	1,684	Lincoln Cathedral	£120.00
2000	13,180	silver proof set, taken from special "Millennium Proof Set" listed on pg. 69	£120.00
2001	1,706	Westminster Abbey	£120.00
2002	1,678	Canterbury Cathedral	£120.00
2002	2,002	gold proof set, taken from special "Golden Jubilee Proof Set".	£1100.00
2003		Gloucester Cathedral	£120.00
2004		Liverpool (Anglican) Cathedral	£120.00
2005		Wakefield Cathedral	£120.00
2006		Guildford Cathedral	£150.00
2007		Manchester Cathedral	
2008		St. Patricks Cathedral, Armagh	
2009		St. Edmundsbury Cathedral, Suffolk	
2010		Derby Cathederal	
2011		Westminster Abbey	
2012		York Minster	
2013		Christ Church Cathedral, Oxford	

The Lunar series 2014 Horse design by Wuon-Gean Ho,
as featured on pages 116 and 117.

The Cover Images.

The images on the cover of this book are all 2014 issues. Top left is the obverse of the First World War £2 coin. To the right of that is the reverse of the floral £1 coin for Scotland followed by the Commonwealth Games 50p reverse. The centre image is the reverse of the Queen Anne commemorative £5 crown coin. Below the crown are, to the left, the Northern Irish floral £1 reverse and to the right, the reverse of the First World War £2 coin.